Brave Little Penguin

Tracey Corderoy Gavin Scott

LITTLE TIGER PRESS
London

Three little roly-poly penguins were having their afternoon snack. Percy and Posy were eating up nicely. But Plip was too busy playing with his favourite toy.

For Mark, with my love xx – T C

To the lovely Gu – G S

LITTLE TIGER PRESS
An imprint of Magi Publications
1 The Coda Centre, 189 Munster Road, London SW6 6AW
www.littletigerpress.com
First published in Great Britain 2011
Text copyright © Tracey Corderoy 2011 • Illustrations copyright © Gavin Scott 2011
Tracey Corderoy and Gavin Scott have asserted their rights to be identified
as the author and illustrator of this work under the Copyright,
Designs and Patents Act, 1988
A CIP catalogue record for this book is
available from the British Library
All rights reserved
ISBN 978-1-84895-243-0
Printed in China
LTP/1800/0203/0511

2 4 6 8 10 9 7 5 3 1

"Hey, Plip," said Percy. "Finish your fish or Wal-the-Wump will snap it up."

"Who's scared of a grumpy old walrus?" giggled Plip. "Not me!"

After their snack, it was swim-time.
But Plip had to keep his toy dry.

"Oh, Plip!" sighed Posy. "Swim like
us or one day Wal-the-Wump might
catch you."

"Wal-the-Wump?" giggled Plip.
"He doesn't scare me!"

When the penguins were too shivery to swim anymore, they played Wal-the-Wump games instead.

"Raggh!" growled Posy.
"I'm Wal. And I'm coming to get you!"

"My turn!" cried Plip, wobbling uphill
and trying to look big and scary.
"I'm Wal-the-Wump and I'll squash
you flat! Hee hee!"

They played together all afternoon.
Then, suddenly, Plip went quiet.
"Hungry?" asked Posy.
"Sleepy?" Percy said.
But Plip just opened his beak
and wailed . . .

"WHERE'S MY SOCKYBUG?"

Everyone searched for
Plip's little sock toy.
    They checked under
the water . . .

then inside all
the caves.

"Where can he be?" sighed Plip.
"He'll be wanting a cuddle."

They were still searching when big snow clouds
gathered and the sky grew dark and stormy.
Percy put a wing around Plip's shoulder.
"You're a big boy now," he said. "You don't
need a baby toy, do you?"

"But he's not a toy," sniffed Plip.
"He's my friend."

They were just about to head back
home when: "Wait!" cried Plip.
"I think I know where I left him!"
He shot away over the hill as
snow began to fall.
"Sockybug!" he called . . .

"I'm coming to get you!"

Percy and Posy raced after Plip
through the tumbling snow.
"Come back!" they yelled.
Then, suddenly, Percy gave a
great gasp, "Oh no!"

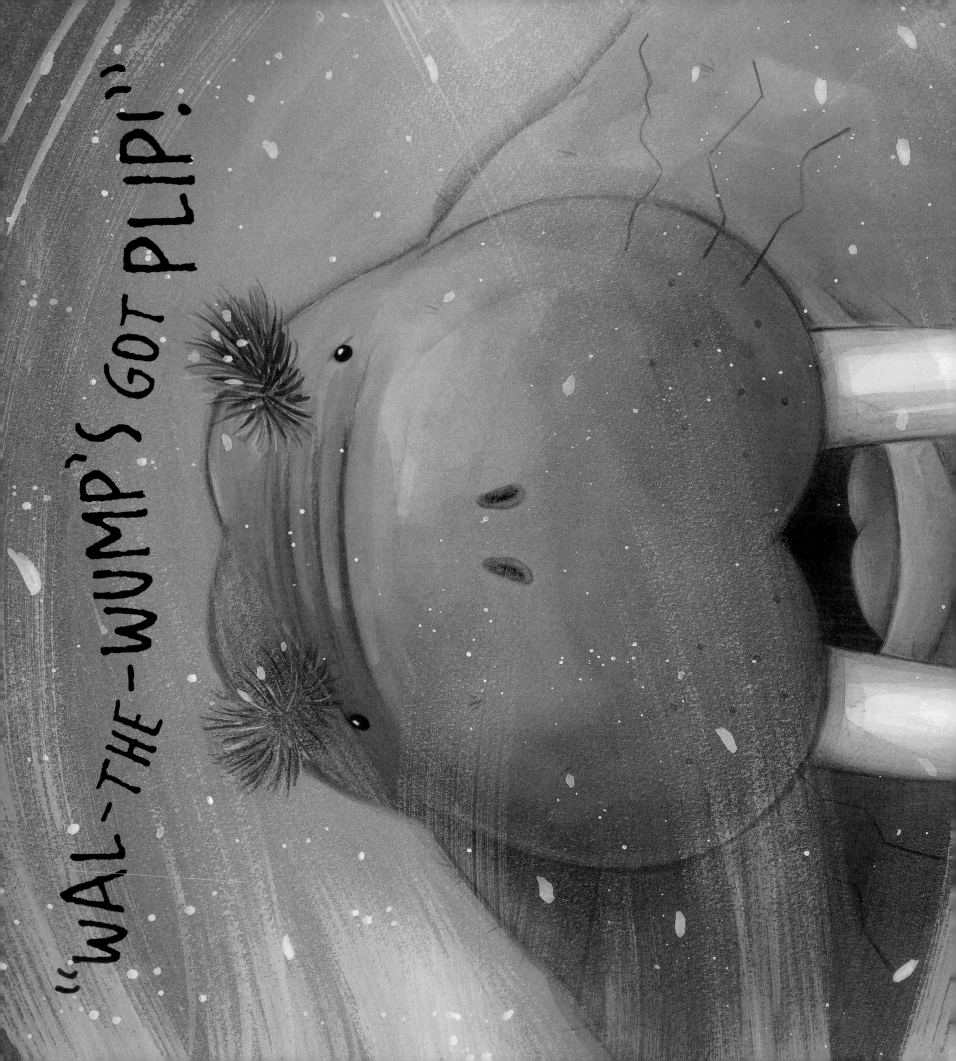

The walrus's enormous teeth
flashed as his jaws opened wide . . .

And Wal let out a gigantic guffaw.
"Tickle, tickle!" chuckled Plip.
Then he turned to his brother and
sister. "Wal found my Sockybug
– look!" he cried.

"HO, HO,

After that, Plip made everyone
their very own Sockybugs.
And from then on, tickle-time
was the best time of the day!

Flower Arranging

Julia Clements

This edition produced exclusively for

WHSMITH

Contents

THE PRINCIPLES OF FLOWER ARRANGING
8

First published 1981 by
Octopus Books Limited
59 Grosvenor Street, London W1

© 1981 Octopus Books Limited

ISBN 0 7064 1504 3

Produced by Mandarin Publishers Limited
22a Westlands Road, Quarry Bay, Hong Kong

Printed in Hong Kong

FLOWERS IN THE HOME
40

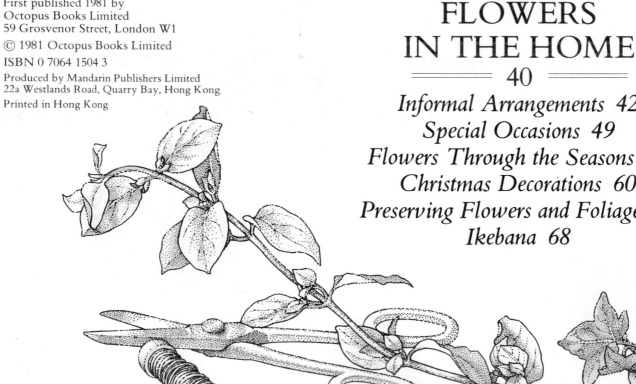

CHURCH FLOWERS and RECEPTIONS
72

THE FLOWER ARRANGER'S GARDEN
104

THE PRINCIPLES OF FLOWER ARRANGING

There are no rigid rules and regulations governing the art of flower arranging. The first secret of success is to have a genuine desire to arrange flowers artistically and to experience pleasure in doing so. However, all artistic achievement benefits from a sound training and it is worth while studying the basic principles. Most people find it necessary to practice the traditional shapes and styles and follow certain guidelines before they are able to interpret their own creative ideas and express themselves freely.

Once you have opened your eyes to all the possibilities there are for using plant material, and have achieved some pleasing results, you will never again walk through a garden or into a florist's shop without assessing the value of a tall branch or some interesting leaves, or the artistic appeal of the brightly coloured flowers.

Selecting Flowers

Flowers grow in many shapes, colours and sizes; some are single blooms, others grow in sprays, while some are made up of small florets which form one large spike or flower. 'What shall I pick?', or, 'What shall I buy?' are the questions many people ask when planning a flower arrangement for the first time. It may be that friends are arriving and you wish to decorate the rooms with fresh flowers to give the house a 'lived-in' and welcoming atmosphere. It may be that you just love flowers and wish to become more efficient at arranging them, or that you have not been able to resist a brightly coloured bunch of flowers from the florist. Whichever it is, take heart, there are tips to be learned to help you not only with the arrangements but also with the choosing of your flowers.

You are lucky if you have a garden which provides you with flowers for cutting, but everyone at some stage finds it necessary to buy their flowers from a florist. This may be because it is a season of the year when flowers are scarce in the garden and, if so, this means they will be expensive since they must be grown in greenhouses or imported from other countries. Another reason for visiting a florist may be that you need a particular variety of flower for a special occasion, such as a wedding reception or cocktail party.

Search around until you find a florist you can rely upon where you know the flowers will be fresh. It is often a false economy to buy cheap flowers as these can be beyond their prime and will not last. A busy, fashionable florist's shop may seem daunting, but in any shop which has a fast turn-over the flowers will be fresh. If you make friends with your florist and show her that you have a genuine interest in flowers, you will find she is very willing to assist you and offer helpful advice.

Always inspect the flowers carefully before buying them. The petals should not be damaged or have any bruise marks on the edges or in the centres and they should feel crisp when felt between your fingers (this sometimes depends very much on the variety of flower). The flower should have a good strong natural colour and must show no signs of fading. Check the centres of flowers which have a mass of petals to see that the centres are tight and not fully open. The foliage of a flower is another indication that the flowers are in peak condition; fresh foliage should show no signs of wilting or turning yellow or brown. Likewise the stems should be crisp and green and not black and slimy when removed from their water.

Remember also that flowers which have been forced will not last as long as those which have grown outside and in their correct season.

When cutting flowers from your garden try to pick them when they are not in full bloom. Experience will show at what stage to cut the different varieties to give maximum lasting ability once they are brought into the house. It is also important to pick the flowers so that the plant will benefit and not be affected any more than is necessary. Try to leave as many buds on the plant as possible and pick long stems which have several flowers on them when the buds are showing the colour of the flowers; green, tight buds will not open in water. Plants which have a great abundance of flowers throughout the season will benefit from heavy picking which encourages new growth and the production of more flowers.

Many beginners ask me whether the vase comes first or the flowers. I would say, it is the setting. You should first study where the flowers are going to be placed, which will help you to decide on the type of vase or container, and this will finally lead you to the correct choice of flowers and foliage. For instance, if your room is fairly large and you wish to make an impressive arrangement for a party, you will need an important container which will lend itself to tall flowers. Whereas, should you wish your dining table to sparkle and be the centre of attraction, you will need to choose shorter-stemmed flowers, so that the arrangement will be low, and include trailing foliage to stretch out at the sides to make a horizontally styled design. Pittosporum, Eucalyptus, Lonicera or Ivy are all good leaves for the sides of a horizontally styled table arrangement; the centre could then be filled in with Carnations, Roses, Sweet Peas or any shorter flowers. Gladioli would not be the best choice for a table arrangement, although I have cut the stems shorter using the tips for the width and the wide-open florets for the centre.

Let us look at what to pick or buy for a large arrangement suitable for a party, a wedding reception or to fill a large space. You will need a selection of different sizes, shapes and forms to make an interesting design. Flowers that are all the same size and length, just put in a vase, will not appear very artistic.

It will help if you think of the three main moves for flower arranging when you select your flowers. Tall and thin flowers which will form the outlines of the arrangement are Delphiniums, Lythrum with its dense star-shaped flowers forming tall spires, Gladioli, Golden Rod, Antirrhinums, Forsythia, Yew and the soft, grey, silky catkins of the Pussy Willow. Fine grasses, bare branches, budded sprays and the green foliage and flowers or berries of the Berberis also come under the 'outline' category.

You will realise in time that these more pointed materials are placed on the outside of the design in order not to hold your interest. Their main function is to lead the eye to the centre of the arrangement where it should be held by the more important flowers.

The rounder, more dominant flowers are used for the centre. Examples are Dahlias, Roses, Chrysanthemums, Paeonies with their large globular flower-heads and Rhododendrons.

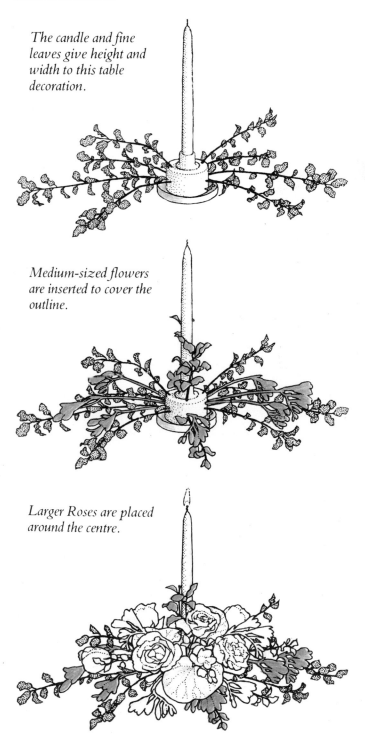

The candle and fine leaves give height and width to this table decoration.

Medium-sized flowers are inserted to cover the outline.

Larger Roses are placed around the centre.

11

Clusters of berries or even a cluster of small flowers can also be placed in the centre of interest as can large leaves or materials of a heavier texture. The centre of interest is usually placed at the base of the tallest stem, and it is from this point that all the stems should appear to emerge.

The final move is to fill in, and here medium and less important flowers are used like Scabious, spray Pinks, spray Chrysanthemums, Daisies, Love-in-a-mist, Geums and Aquilegias to name but a few. You will also need some leaves to give depth and to place around the centre to unite the stems, and perhaps some trails of Ivy or Honeysuckle to flow downwards, so uniting the flowers to the container.

An alternative method is to cover the outline first with the medium-sized flowers and then to finish the design with the dominant flowers in the centre.

If you are faced with the problem of having flowers all of one kind and size, the answer is to follow the same idea as for a mixed selection. Cut the flowers to different lengths using the long stems for the outline, the medium length stems for filling in and the shorter, yet larger flowers for the centre. If the arrangement requires a dominant centre, you can cluster a few blooms together or add some grapes, pine cones, leaves or berries, depending on the season and what is available.

It is important to buy or pick flowers which are in scale and proportion to the vase they are to be placed in, just as it is important that the vase is in proportion to the setting where it will stand. Small delicate vases made from china or glass will fit well on a side table under a lamp, filled with small flowers such as Pinks, Cornflowers or Freesias with their funnel-shaped flowers and beautiful fragrance. If the arrangement is to be placed in a high position like a mantelshelf or wall sconce, try to include Honeysuckle, Ivy or Periwinkle to trail downwards. Narrow, tall vases will fit in well with high-ceilinged rooms and tall-stemmed flowers, but if the setting is one of a cosy room with a low-beamed ceiling, the arrangement should be shorter and more rounded.

It is not only the form, shape and size of the flowers which must be considered but also the colour. If the walls of the room are dark, then light-coloured flowers will show up with greater importance, whereas if the room is light in appearance, greater effect will be gained from using dark strong colours. Personal preference will also enter into the decision of what you pick or buy, but, whatever your choice, try to obtain flowers of different sizes and shapes even if they are all the same colour.

I often estimate how many stems I shall need for an arrangement. For a fairly large design I will pick or buy nine tall stems for the outline, seven large round flowers to place down the centre and approximately twelve stems of a medium size for filling in and flowing forward low over the rim. I like to include a spray of leaves for the background and some bolder leaves, such as Hosta (Plantain Lily), Bergenia or Paeony around the centre, and a few trails for the sides and the front. Before the flowers are arranged they must be conditioned, for no one wishes to spend time and effort creating a work of art with flowers, only to find them drooping the next day.

Conditioning and Care of Cut Flowers

Having chosen your flowers they will last longer if they are conditioned before being arranged. This applies to all cut flowers, whether they have been picked from the garden, bought from a florist or received as a gift. The temptation to arrange the flowers immediately must be avoided so that your hard work and design will give pleasure for the longest time possible.

Different types of flowers require different types of conditioning, but as soon as any flower or foliage is picked it is deprived of its natural source of water and the sooner it is put into water the longer it will last. Here is a list of suggestions to help you condition your flowers, remembering that much depends upon when, and under what conditions, the flowers were picked.

❧ Always pick flowers before they are fully mature.

❧ Flowers should, whenever possible, be picked at night or early in the morning when loss of water is at its lowest. During the day flowers lose water through evaporation (this is called transpiration).

Woody-stemmed flowers should have their lower leaves removed and their stems split before they are placed in water.

When you pick flowers from your own garden, take a bucket filled with water so that the stems can be placed in water as soon as they are cut.

Wild flowers, once they have been picked, should immediately be wrapped in wet newspaper or polythene. This will keep them fresh on the journey home. Once at home, the stems should be re-cut and placed in deep water overnight.

All flowers should have their lower leaves stripped off and their stems re-cut under water. This is particularly important for hollow-stemmed plants as it will avoid an airlock forming in the stem which will prevent the flower from taking water. The stems should be cut at an angle which will give a wider exposed area than a straight horizontal cut, allowing the flower to take in the maximum amount of water. The angle-cut stem, when placed in a vase, will rest on the lower point of the angled cut. A flat-ended stem would lie flush with the bottom of the vase, obstructing the flow of water up the stem. The re-cut flowers should be left in deep water overnight in a dark airy place before being arranged. This treatment will harden the stems and allow the flowers to become fully loaded with water.

All woody-stemmed flowers, such as Lilac, Viburnum, outdoor Chrysanthemums, Roses and other flowering trees and shrubs should have some of their lower leaves removed and the bottom 4 cm (1½ inches) of their stems split or crushed before they are placed in deep water. I prefer to split the ends as crushing causes bruising and allows bacteria to form. Using a sharp knife or florists' scissors, scrape the lower 4 cm (1½ inches) of the outside

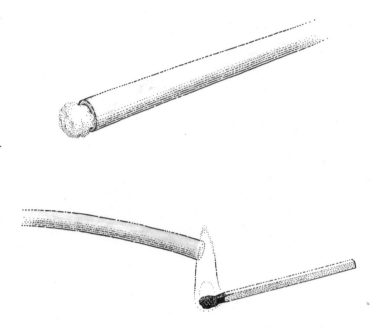

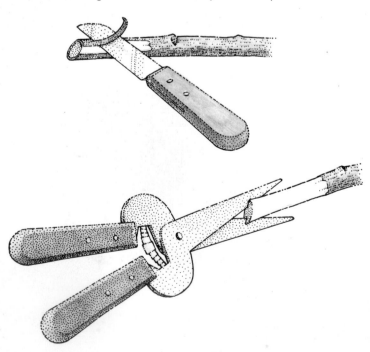

covering (the bark) off the stem to expose the inner tissue. Split the exposed stem lengthwise.

Always remove the white portion at the stem ends of bulbous flowers, such as early Tulips and Daffodils, as they only drink from the green portion.

Hold the stem ends of Daffodils, Narcissi, Hyacinths and similar flowers under warm running water to remove the sticky sap they exude. If this is not done the sap forms a seal over the end of the stem making it more difficult for the flower to take in water.

Jointed stems, such as Carnations and Sweet Williams, should have their stems cut at an angle just above one of the joints.

Certain flowers, such as Delphiniums and Lupins, will benefit if the hollow stems are filled with water after cutting and then plugged with cotton wool, before being left overnight in deep water.

Lupins are best picked when only the three lower rings of florets are open. The stems should be cut straight, not at an angle. This helps the Lupin spire to remain straight as they have a tendency to bend into a kink.

Dahlias, Poppies, Euphorbias and other flowers exude a white substance called latex when they are picked, which will quickly form an impenetrable skin over the end of the stem, depriving the flower of water. This can be avoided if the cut stem-ends are allowed to stand in 5 cm (2 inches) of very hot water for about ten seconds. Alternatively, the ends can be singed by holding them in a flame for a few seconds. Both these methods disperse the latex layer and stop any further flow.

Roses will last longer if the lower leaves and thorns are

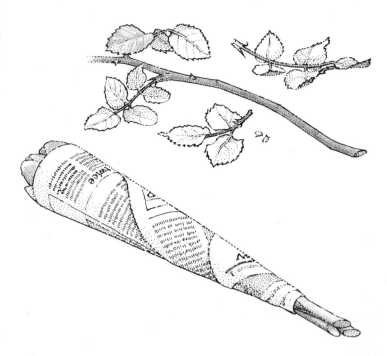

removed and the stem ends split, before they are placed in water. Wilting Roses, which have been left out of water for some time or have arrived by post, should be treated in the same way before being placed in near-boiling water to which a teaspoon of sugar has been added. There are also several commercial products, such as Chrysal, which when added to the water, instead of sugar, will revive wilting flowers. Most flowers will last longer if sugar is added to the water in the container they are arranged in. (This does not apply to Daffodils and Narcissi.) Use one teaspoon of sugar to one pint of water.

❧ Tulips will always turn to face the light. Pierce the stem just under the head with a pin and then wrap them in newspaper so that the stem and flower are well supported. Plunge the newspaper-wrapped flowers into deep water and leave overnight.

❧ Hellebores and Anemones will stand up strongly if a pin is drawn down the side of the stem from top to bottom, before leaving them to stand in deep tepid or warm water, prior to arranging.

❧ Gourds, which form the basis of many dried arrangements, should be picked when fully ripe and the skins are hard, then placed on a sheet of newspaper in a warm room or cupboard to dry. (Try to leave a short stem on the gourd as this makes wiring easier, if needed.) They should be checked regularly and any transpiration wiped off with a cloth.

❧ Blossoming sprays can be forced into early flowering if they are first submerged in warm water to swell the buds and then, after slitting the stem ends, placed in warm water in a warm room. This will only work if the blossom is picked when the buds are swollen and ready to burst.

❧ Mimosa or Acacia is not renowned for its long-lasting ability and has a tendency to turn dark and lose its beautiful bright yellow colour. This can be avoided if it is kept stored in a polythene bag until needed. Just before it is required for arranging, dip the flowers first in cold water and then in hot. Mimosa will last longer if the stem ends are split and placed in 8 cm (3 inches) of near-boiling water to which a teaspoon of sugar has been added. Later fill up and arrange. If you put Chrysal powder into the water in which the flowers are to be arranged, this will help them to live longer. Mimosa will not remain fluffy for long indoors; but even when it is dry it is still attractive.

❧ Leaves and sprays of greenery should be submerged in water for some hours before being arranged, but be careful as some leaves which are soaked too long lose their texture. Only experience will tell you how long to soak different varieties of leaves. Soaking does not apply to leaves which have a woolly texture or are heavily covered with hairs. Lamb's Tongue (*Stachys lanata*) is one of these varieties and will soak up water like a sponge, resulting in it losing its beautiful grey tones. Woolly textured leaves should have their stems dipped into boiling water for one to two minutes, taking care to protect the leaves from the hot steam by wrapping them in paper. The leaves should then be conditioned in shallow water.

❧ *Begonia rex* and other rather soft-leaved house plants, if cut and used in decorations, should first be submerged for some hours in water to which a teaspoon of sugar has been added.

❧ When placing flowers in deep water to condition

them, make sure the containers are spotlessly clean and are the correct size for the flowers. Do not place short-stemmed flowers in with long-stemmed ones as these may crush the smaller flowers or drink so much water that the shorter stems are left clear of the water.

❧ Always have warm water in the container or vase you are arranging into as this will prevent the ends of the stems from drying while you work. A tablet of charcoal in the water will help to keep it pure. Check the level of the water every day and top up with tepid water if necessary.

❧ Keep all flower arrangements away from the hot sun or cold draughts, even if this means you must move them from time to time. It will be worth it.

❧ Exotic flowers, such as Anthuriums, Orchids, Strelitzias, although very long lasting, will benefit if the stem ends are re-cut after a week to remove the brown stain which often appears. If this is allowed to remain it will attract bacteria.

❧ A fine spray of water around the arrangement will help to counteract the loss of moisture through transpiration. These sprays can be purchased from garden centres and hardwear shops. There are also commercial products, such as Clear Life and S.100, which can be sprayed lightly over the arrangement to close the pores of the plant material. This is particularly beneficial for exhibitions and occasions where the flowers must last for a long time.

❧ Camellia, Rhododendron, Laurel and other large-surfaced shiny leaves can have their shine prolonged if they are wiped over occasionally with a damp cloth sprinkled with a few drops of oil. There is also a commercial product, called Leaf Shine, which can be bought from florists and garden centres, which does the same job.

❧ When using floral foam to hold the flowers in place, make sure it has been well saturated with water. This will take about half-an-hour. Leave a space at the back of the vase where more water can be added daily.

The only way to perfect the conditioning of flowers is to experiment, but remember: (1) that all flowers should have their stems cut under water and then be left to stand in deep water for several hours in a dark, dry and airy place, before being arranged; (2) all woody-type stems should be split; and (3) most leaves should be submerged in water for a few hours before use. Use warm water in your container and do not forget to top it up each day. If you follow these rules your flowers should stay fresh and be a source of joy to all who see them.

Early Acacia (Mimosa), pink Nerines, large Auratum Lilies, blue Irises, Roses, Chrysanthemums, Narcissi, Anemones and Hydrangeas make up this colourful group.

Materials and Equipment

You do not need a lot of equipment to make a start with flower arranging, for you can begin simply with a container, a pair of florists' scissors and a pin-holder or a piece of wire-netting. However, as you progress you will find, just as a good cook requires a number of different implements, or an artist requires various brushes and paints, that you will need more items to enable you to create various styles for different occasions. So let us look at some of the items a good flower arranger will use.

Pin-Holders and Well-Holders

Pin-holders Flower pin-holders are an essential piece of a flower arranger's equipment. They are made in many sizes and shapes, the most common shape being circular varying from 2.5 cm (1 inch) to 8 cm (3 inches) in diameter. Oval and rectangular pin-holders are also available. Pin-holders are mainly used in shallow dishes and to give extra-firm support for the angled and heavy stems used in large, tall and wide arrangements. Metal pin-holders have a number of closely packed nails held point upward in a heavy lead base, and can be obtained from most florists' shops, garden centres and department stores. Extra-heavy holders containing larger nails can be obtained for holding weighty branches. Others have very fine, sharp pins and are suitable for flowers and foliage which have especially thin and delicate stems, such as Sweet Peas, Freesias and small spring flowers. By selecting the correct pin-holder, almost all flowers can be easily fixed into the pattern you wish.

If you find your pin-holder is inclined to topple, try fixing it firmly to the bottom of the container with plasticine or adhesive clay. Press three round knobs of plasticine or adhesive clay onto the dry base of the holder, then press it down onto the dry surface of the base of the dish, giving it a twist as you do so. Florists sell a special substance which will hold the pin-holder permanently in place and this is ideal when you are using a container which is used only for flower arranging. As you become more proficient at flower arranging you should not need plasticine to hold the pin-holder in place since if your design is well balanced, as it should be, it will not topple. However, in the beginning you will find plasticine very helpful.

Pin-holders are also useful in tall containers, especially the tubular sort which are so tall that the flowers placed in them fall to the bottom so that only the heads are visible. This can be overcome by filling more than half of the container with sand or wet newspaper and then placing a pin-holder on this false surface. Hot candle wax can be poured across the sand to create a firm platform for the pin-holder or, alternatively, the pin-holder can be placed in a shallow tin of water.

NOTE: Pin-holders are not suitable for placing in clear glass containers as they can be seen through the glass. As an alternative, try using a small roll of crumpled wire-netting at the top of the vase opening, or criss-cross the top with adhesive tape or florists' tape to form a grid. The ends of the tape should be cut just below the outer rim of the vase and these can be held in place with a continuous length of tape stuck around the outer edge. The flowers and foliage can then be inserted into the openings between the tape. Leaves and foliage can be trained over the rim of the vase to hide the wire or tape.

Well-holders A well-holder is a variation of the pin-holder and is simply a pin-holder welded into a heavy, metal, shallow cup. The cup-like base holds the water, enabling it to be used in shallow baskets, on flat bases or other items which do not hold water. A well-holder can also be used for placing behind an ornament or collection of fruits where it will be well hidden. A piece of water-soaked floral foam pressed onto the pins of the holder adds extra holding power when certain downward angles are required.

Pin-holders and well-holders are available in a variety of shapes and sizes.

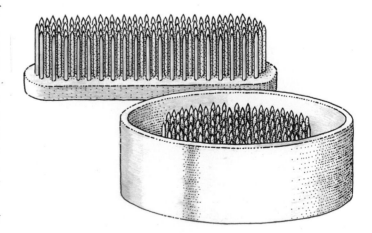

Wire-Netting

Holders are very important, for it is almost impossible to make a well designed picture with flowers unless you use some kind of holder to keep the flowers firmly in place. For upright classical vases a piece of crumpled wire-netting gives excellent support, providing you push it well down into the vase and allow some of it to rise above the rim.

Wire-netting can be obtained from most hardware shops where it is sold in metres or yards. A 5 cm (2 inch) mesh is the best for general use, though a finer mesh is more suitable for small flowers.

The wire should be cut according to the size and shape of your container. If you mean to fill the vase completely it is best to have the wire-netting twice the width and twice the height of the vase. It takes a little time to fix the wire-netting firmly in the container, but it is time well spent. Make sure that it reaches just above the rim of the container, do not crumple it too tightly and leave a fair amount of space in the centre where most of the stems will meet.

The cut ends of the mesh can be pressed over the rim of the vase to hold the netting in place, or string can be threaded through the mesh at the edge of the container, pulled tight and tied around the top outer edge of the vase. Two strong rubber bands will also hold the netting firmly to the vase if they are passed over the top of the netting at right angles to one another and down under the base of the bowl (this is only suitable for small containers). Reel wire can be used for larger containers: use the wire in the same way as the rubber bands and secure it at the base of the vase or around the stem by twisting the two loose ends of wire together.

I often use a pin-holder under the wire-netting to give added support to the stems and I find that I can get the quickest and best results this way. This method is particularly good for a tall container with a wide opening, such as a compote stand or an urn, for the stems placed vertically down through the wire and onto the pin-holder will be held firmly. Other stems can be inserted almost horizontally at the sides and the front of the container. I also use this method in a shallow cake tin which I then place on a silver or white china cake stand.

A pin-holder can be placed on a false platform of sand and wax in a tall container. This prevents the flowers falling to the bottom.
The cut ends of wire-netting can be attached to the rim of the container to secure it in place.
As an alternative to pin-holders, clear adhesive tape can be attached in a criss-cross pattern over the mouth of a glass container.
Cones to give extra height and candle cups for use in narrow-necked containers are useful items of equipment.

Scissors, Secateurs and Knives

Scissors Special flower or florists' scissors can be purchased from horticultural suppliers. These are not expensive and will prove to be a very good investment. They have short blades, one of which is serrated, and usually have a small notch at the base of the blades for cutting wire. With care and regular oiling, these scissors will last a long time. Although you may think you can manage with ordinary scissors, you will find many occasions when they will not cut through thick woody stems and will squash, not cut, the stems of your flowers.

Secateurs Most keen gardeners will possess a pair of secateurs but although they are useful to flower arrangers for cutting extra-thick, strong branches, they are not essential. Wire cutters are also useful for cutting wire-netting, stub wires and reel wire and this will save your flower scissors which otherwise would have to be used for this job.

Knives A good sharp knife is useful for scraping and cleaning plant material but it must be very sharp so that it makes a clean cut through stems and does not simply crush them. Remember to keep all sharp knives and pointed scissors out of the reach of children.

Buckets and Watering Cans

Buckets These are used for soaking the stems of flowers which are being conditioned prior to arranging. It is best to have several different sizes, for if small short-stemmed flowers are put to soak with larger flowers they may be crushed. Buckets with side handles are more practical than those with only one handle as the handle may damage the blooms when the bucket is being carried. Try not to use your buckets for anything other than flowers and foliage as any trace of detergent will harm the flowers. The buckets must be kept spotlessly clean and all traces of plant material must be removed after the flowers have finished soaking.

Watering cans The most useful kind of watering can is one with a long thin spout which will enable you to top up your flower arrangements without disturbing the flowers and foliage.

The twisted piece of dry tree root was placed across the mouth of this modern pottery container to give width and interest to the vertical design. The flame-coloured Lilies were cut to different lengths and inserted one below the other into the pin-holder in the base of the container.

Cones and Candle Cups

Cones Metal or plastic cones are invaluable to the decorator when more height is needed in an arrangement than the tallest stems can give. This applies to pedestal groups for parties, weddings or church arrangements. Cones can be obtained from garden centres or your florist should be able to get them for you. They can be used singly or more than one can be mounted with adhesive tape or wire to a garden bamboo stick. The stick is then inserted into the floral foam or crumpled wire-netting, whichever you are using. Several cones placed at different levels can be used. The cones should be filled with water or water-soaked floral foam before the flowers are inserted. Green is the usual colour of the cones, but they can be spray painted any colour to fit in with the colour scheme of your arrangement. Cones should never be visible when the arrangement is finished.

Candle cups These are useful gadgets which can be obtained from florists' shops and are made from plastic or metal. Plastic candle cups are usually gold, silver, black or white but if none of these fits in with the colour of your container they can be sprayed any shade with one of the many aerosol spray paints, available from hardware shops and department stores. Candle cups are shaped like a shallow bowl with a stem at the base and are mainly used in candlesticks, bottles or any narrow-necked containers. A piece of plasticine, or one of the many sticky substances now widely available, can be placed under the bowl part of the candle cup. This will hold the cup firmly in place.

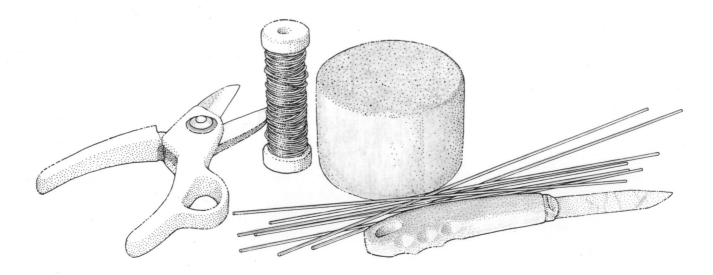

Reel Wire and Stub Wire

Reel wire This is sold on spools and is a thin wire used for several different purposes in flower arranging. It can be used for securing crumpled wire-netting to containers and is also used for wiring single leaves, pine cones, delicate florets or any plant material which has no stem. The wire provides a false stem as well as strengthening leaves and other floppy foliage. Reel wire is used when a group of stems need to be bound together or attached to a garland or swag.

Stub wires These come in a variety of lengths: 18–46 cm (7–18 inches) long. They also vary in thickness and it is useful to have a mixed selection of thin 0.71mm (22 gauge), medium 0.90 mm (20 gauge) and thick 1.25 mm (18 gauge) stub wires. Note that the lower the imperial gauge the thicker the wire and the lower the metric gauge the thinner the wire. These wires are used mainly by florists whose skills fashion lovely bouquets and corsages, but amateurs often need these wires to make false stems and to lengthen short-stemmed flowers. Always use a thickness of wire which is in scale with the flower or foliage you are wiring. A thick stub wire will rip through the delicate petals of a floret, while a thin wire will not have the strength to support a heavy bloom.

Bases

A base is any item on which the flower arrangement rests. It can be a flat, water-resistant mat to protect furniture, or something used to raise a flower arrangement. Today, with the world-wide increase in flower arranging, a base is also used to accent the colour of the flowers at a show. One or more thinner bases can be placed cross-wise to each other to add a note of distinction.

Floral Foams

Floral foams, which can be bought under several brand names, are plastic substances which absorb water. The main difference between the various makes is in their density. Use a dense foam for heavy floral material and a lighter one for delicate stems. If you have difficulty inserting thin soft stems into the foam, pierce it first with a fine knitting needle or bodkin. Foam comes in different sizes and can be oblong, cylindrical or round in shape. It is usually green in colour which fits in well with the foliage (other coloured foam is not always water absorbent and is used only for dried arrangements). It is not always possible to buy foam that is the right size for your container but a large piece can easily be cut to the correct size with a knife. Always cut the foam so that it sticks up above the rim of the container. Large vases do not necessarily have to be completely filled with foam and a piece wedged in the top of the container will hold the flowers in place.

Dry foam should be soaked in water which is deep enough to cover it, and it is ready to use when it starts to fill and sinks to the bottom. Leave the foam to soak until it is completely saturated; this should take about half-an-hour. Once it is full it can be placed in the container.

Although floral foam is not suitable for all arrangements, it is particularly good for show work and special party occasions. It has the great advantage of allowing you to place your flowers at any angle. Even flowers and foliage which swerve downwards will be held firmly in place while still being able to absorb moisture.

If the foam cracks and breaks up when heavy stems are inserted, use some other method or cover it with wire-netting. When an extra-large piece of floral foam is needed for 'tree pots' or free-standing arrangements, two or more pieces can be held together with wire-netting.

Sphagnum moss is the most common moss used in flower arranging. It is used for lining hanging baskets, covering bowls of bulbs and concealing wire-netting, pin-holders, cones and any other aid which needs hiding. It can also be used as a base for flowers as it holds moisture well. Sphagnum moss is found in woods and bog lands and can be kept fresh for a considerable length of time if soaked in water and then stored in a polythene bag.

Club mosses are useful for placing on the surface of containers that are planted with pot plants which like plenty of water. If the moss is removed carefully from its natural growing place and placed on the compost around the plants it will continue to grow.

Containers

A flower container today can be almost any receptacle that will hold water. The term 'vase' refers mainly to containers which are tall, thin and specifically made for holding long-stemmed flowers.

Wall brackets seem to have been the first containers designed to hold flowers in the home. The first of these were produced by the Leeds pottery in 1745 and were followed in 1750 by salt-glazed stone-ware brackets from the Staffordshire pottery. The famous Wedgwood factory made urn-shaped bough pots in 1770, a shape which is still popular among flower arrangers.

Today, due to the tremendous upsurge of interest in flower arranging, a wide variety of containers can be bought. Many can also be found in the home. These do not have to be traditional shapes and can include coffee pots, dishes, plates, cake stands, glasses, goblets, bottles, as well as fine china and silver ware. They can be made from metal, pewter, pottery, copper, wood or any other water-resistant material. Whichever you choose, all have a particular role to play in holding flowers for various occasions.

Choosing a Container

Choosing a container is important and as much care and attention should be given to this as to the choice of flowers. The container and the flowers must unite so that one does not dominate the other. The container should have as much interest of colour, texture, form and scale as the flowers and foliage which are to be placed in it. Another point to consider when making your choice is the setting in which the flower-filled container will be placed. A tall thin vase is not suitable for a coffee table – a china cup and saucer filled with delicate flowers would be

much more fitting. Natural-coloured containers seem to unite well with most coloured flowers, but make sure the shape fits in with the general style of your home.

The style of your design will also determine the shape of the container. The upright classical container filled with crumpled wire-netting lends itself best to the formal mass arrangements, whereas a low open dish used with a pin-holder is preferable for a modern linear design. A tall tubular-shaped container is ideal for branches arranged in the Japanese style and a wine glass will look effective filled with Lily of the Valley, or similar flowers, which need no support and form an informal arrangement. Special flowers, such as Orchids or Roses, look especially elegant if arranged into fine china or silver containers.

Baskets

Baskets of all kinds have many uses for plant and flower arranging. The half-moon shaped shopping baskets make ideal containers for pot plants which can be hung from a wall or door. Flowers and foliage can be arranged in them by either inserting a watertight container inside the basket or, if it is made with a close weave, by lining with polythene and then wet floral foam. Flower arrangements in these types of baskets look especially attractive if Ivy or Tradescantia are allowed to trail down over the edge of the basket.

By lining baskets with waterproof tins or dishes, old fishing creels, wicker handbags, picnic hampers, basket-ware trays and even waste paper baskets become effective containers for fruit, flowers and leaves, particularly in a rustic setting. Even a summer straw hat or holiday coolie hat upturned and set on a table will provide a good base for a plant or leaf grouping. In fact there is endless potential for any form of straw, rush or palm woven baskets used as flower and plant containers.

Shells

Shells make interesting containers for growing plants or for cut flowers and foliage, their attractive interiors sometimes being left uncovered. An empty shell backed with sea-fern and grasses can make an interesting arrangement. Sprays of grey *Artemisia absinthium*, or pink Rosebay Willowherb which has gone to seed, on a pin-holder in the base of an upturned clam shell can give the impression of plumes waving in the sea. Placing the shell on a black wooden base or small tray protects the furniture and adds to the picture.

Flowers and foliage can be held firmly in a shell if the shell is packed with floral foam, moss or sand. Whichever method you use, make sure the filling is kept constantly wet. A giant shell can have a small, foam-filled container laid inside it which can be secured with plasticine, but be careful the water does not spill out if the shell has curved lips or wavy edges.

Shells come in all shapes, sizes, colours and textures. The large green snail shells, which are iridescent on the outside and pearly inside, are so beautiful that it is a shame to place anything inside them but a few fine, tall green sprays. These will not only give height but accentuate the beauty of the shell. Small shells of any kind can be thrown into the shallow water around the base of a pin-holder to make interesting underwater decorations.

Common scallop shells are not to be shunned either as they can make delightful individual place setting arrangements, or be grouped together for a table centre-piece. To do this, mix some plaster filler powder with water into a thick consistency. Pile this onto a base and insert five scallop shells in a circle near the base; next place three shells slightly higher and nearer the centre of the pile of filler, rather like the petals of a flower. Finally place a single shell on the top. The shells can be filled with flowers and foliage or small Sedum or Echeveria plants.

OPPOSITE *and* LEFT: *Baskets, food jars and all kinds of kitchen utensils can be used to hold snippets from the garden.*

Bottles

Bottles make fascinating containers. Stone cider and pickling jars filled with wheat, grasses and berries in the autumn look attractive placed on an old oak or pine dresser or in front of other country-style backgrounds.

Dark green wine bottles and decanters should be washed out well and scrubbed inside with a bottle brush. If the bottle is made from clear glass, a few drops of food colouring added to the water will look attractive and will also help to conceal the stems. Small bottles, such as old scent bottles or small old blue or clear glass medicine bottles, when used in conjunction with small flowers and feather-like foliage and placed on a dressing table or bedside cupboard in a guest room, are a welcoming sight to visitors.

Home-made Containers

More adventurous arrangers can experiment with making their own containers. Tall or shallow round biscuit tins can be painted with a mixture of paint and sawdust which gives a rough-textured finish. Alternatively, rush table mats can be glued around them.

Tins of all shapes and sizes can be converted into useful containers. Cement, which can be purchased from 'do-it-yourself' shops in small bags, can be mixed with clear glossy or matt varnish or gloss paint. This mixture can then be spread onto the outside of the tins. The paint or varnish helps the cement to adhere to the smooth surface. To vary the texture of the surface, imprints of buttons and other small objects can be made by pressing them into the wet surface of the cement. If the wet cement is stroked

onto the outside of the tin with a fork it will give the appearance of ridged wood. Pastel-coloured effects can be obtained by adding a few drops of coloured ink or food colouring to white plaster powder.

There is a wide variety of patterned tins on the market but if you cannot find one of a suitable colour you can always paint it yourself. In fact, any metal or enamel pieces of kitchen equipment can be painted a different colour, such as colanders, old kettles, weighing scales and old bread bins. I once painted a metal colander with mauve paint, planting it later with pink and purple Petunias and hanging it over my studio door.

An old gramophone record can be moulded into a container if it is first soaked in very hot water to soften it. Seal the central hole with hot wax to make it watertight.

Another idea is to make a raised base, using four cotton reels and a 45 × 30 cm (18 × 12 inch) piece of wood. Nail or glue the cotton reels to the wood approximately 5 cm (2 inches) in from the corners. Screw or nail an empty tin onto the top of this home-made table, either in the centre or to one side. Paint the whole thing with matt black paint. If you coat the tin with vinegar and allow it to dry before painting it, the paint will more readily adhere to the tin. Place a smaller tin inside the tin nailed to the wood to make it watertight.

Using a bottle, a cork and a tin pie-dish, a container can be made which will look most attractive when it is filled with short-stemmed flowers and drooping foliage. Screw or nail the cork to the centre of the underside of the tin. Drop candle-grease or sealing wax round the nail to prevent any leakage of water. Insert the cork into the bottle which should be weighted first by filling it with water or gravel. The flowers and foliage are then arranged in the tin.

Driftwood and Bark

Driftwood can be turned into a container as well as being used as a base or incorporated into a design. All wood which has been weathered by rain, wind or snow is called driftwood and does not only apply to wood which has been in the sea.

Wash the wood well, scrubbing it with a solution of detergent, disinfectant and water. Place the wood to dry in a warm place. Once it is dry it can be trimmed into the shape you require with a knife or small saw if the branches are thick. The loose bark must be scraped off, but if you wish to have the branch without any bark at all, soak it in water for a few days before scraping it. Because the driftwood has been lying exposed to the elements, it will more than likely have a few rotten patches where the wood has turned soft. These areas can be scraped out and the hole lined with foil or polythene to make a container for flowers. If the piece of driftwood will not stand steadily on a surface it will have to be secured to a wooden base by screwing a nail up through the base of the wood and into the driftwood.

If the piece of driftwood is large, it may be better to secure it to a tin or a wooden base with plaster of Paris. The plaster should be mixed with water to form a stiff paste. Pile this in the centre of the base or onto the tin and, working quickly, press the driftwood into the plaster. Paint the tin and the plaster a neutral shade so that it fits in well with the colour of the driftwood.

Bark can make a natural, textured container. A large intact piece of semi-circular bark can be lined with foil or polythene and then filled with moss or floral foam. This type of container fits in well with a country setting.

Containers for Plants

Containers are not just used for flower arranging but also for plants. These containers can be delicate or coarse – glass or silver for delicate ferns like the Maidenhair Fern, and wood or pottery for heavy leaves and seed-heads. Baskets also make ideal containers for mixed groups of plants, while copper, brass and pewter are often the best choice for leaves and plants which have a similar colouring. A plant of Lamb's Tongue (*Stachys lanata*) transferred from the garden to a pewter mug can make an inexpensive and appealing decoration on a writing desk. A *Grevillea robusta* with its fern-like leaves will have a ravishing and long-lasting effect if placed in a copper or brass container. The various combinations are endless and time spent in the search for new ideas is often very rewarding.

Shapes and Styles

Style is the way in which we express our own personal thoughts, whether it is in painting, writing, acting, flower arranging or even the way we dress. By looking back you can see how the style of flower arranging has changed and developed through the ages. During the Victorian era a mass arrangement was mostly designed and executed in a circular style and it was not until the twentieth century that the triangular design became the main shape for mass arrangements.

Newcomers to flower arranging might well ask why it is important to learn the different styles, when all they want to do is to arrange a bowl of flowers artistically. This may have been their primary reason for making a start, but as they progress they will realise that it is necessary to expand their knowledge and technique. This will enable them to make shapes to suit different positions in the home or wherever they may be asked to arrange flowers.

For example, a classical *triangular* shape is suitable for the centre of a table which is backed by a wall, whereas an *asymmetrical* (off-centre) triangle is used for the end of such a table which has items standing at the opposite end.

A central table in a large hall or room may require an all-round design (equal all round), but on a corner table in a modern flat a tall arrangement with a *vertical* emphasis to the design would be appropriate. A *horizontal* arrangement having no vertical lines in it is often used for a long table. A *rectangular* 'L' shape is often used for the end of a mantelshelf where a central arrangement would be too large or tall. An arrangement which is placed off-centre must be balanced by ornaments or other objects placed at the opposite end of the mantelshelf or surface.

The *Hogarth curve* is named after the eighteenth-century English painter Hogarth, who described the flowing but irregular line of an 'S' curve as 'the line of beauty'.

The container in which to arrange the flowers for this style should have a tall stem which allows for the downward curve of plant material. Start by placing a piece of floral foam in the container and securing it well. Try to select flowers and foliage which have a natural curve. If this proves impossible, flexible foliage and stems can be made to curve by gently bending them into the required shape and then wiring the tip of the curve to the main stem. This ensures that the branch remains in the correct shape while it is being conditioned in deep water overnight. Place tall curved stems of foliage and flowers in the top left-hand side of the foam. Next place similar floral material in the right side of the foam so that it swerves in an identical curve down to the left. The tip of the tallest top stem should ideally be in a direct, vertical line with the lowest tip of the bottom curve. (This style can be arranged to flow to the left or to the right.) Cover the curve with flowers, placing short, dominant flowers on the inside of the curve. Fill in with small flowers and foliage always keeping within the lines of the curve.

There is no end to the variations of styles which can be used with flowers, for fashions are always changing, as do settings. For instance, the styles the Victorians used with their flowers in circular masses are very different from

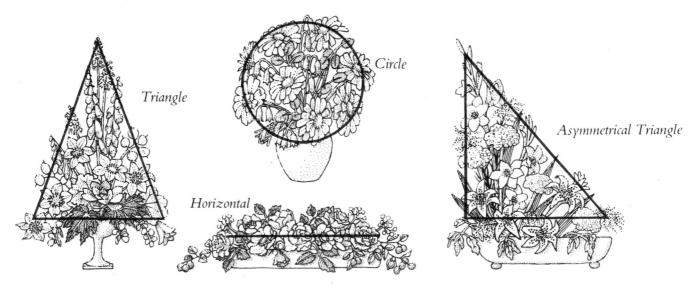

Triangle

Circle

Horizontal

Asymmetrical Triangle

arrangements required for a contemporary home. However, once you have practised different styles and have gained the confidence of knowing how and where to place flowers, you are left free to choose and arrange your flowers in whatever style you like. But remember that practice makes perfect – just as a pianist cannot learn to express himself to the best advantage without learning musical scales, so it is with flower arranging. It is the basic practice which will carry you to full artistry with flowers.

The Mass or Formal Style

Mass arrangements contain many flowers and can be divided into two main types, the 'period' mass and the 'modern' mass. 'Formal' refers to arrangements which are concerned with the occasion rather than the line of the arrangement.

Formal designs call for formal vases, so avoid heavy, shallow pottery dishes, so necessary for modern linear designs, and use instead silver, glass or fine china containers. Take care that the container blends happily with the décor and furniture of your home, and remember that the shape of the arrangement should suit the position in which it is to be placed.

Flowers such as Sweet Peas, Roses, Lilies, Orchids, Delphiniums and special varieties of flowers are considered suitable for mass arrangements. Colour is also relevant: mauve, purple, pink, crimson and blue are all suitable. Small, elegant containers filled with tiny precious flowers and leaves lend an air of formality, especially when placed on antique furniture, perhaps under a lamp.

To make a formal triangular arrangement, first decide where the arrangement will stand. It is always best to arrange the flowers with the container *in situ*, but make sure the surface under the container is well protected with a polythene sheet. Make the outline of the triangle first, then establish the centre with the flowers pointing forward and finally fill in from the outside making sure the stems all converge in the centre. Make the arrangement taller if the rooms are high, shorter if they are low.

The Modern Style

To make an original modern design, do not be afraid to use strong or contrasting colours; nor must you fear heights, for tall designs are more representative of the modern style than a squat arrangement. The value of

This arrangement of dry Honeysuckle Vine and pink Roses complements the modern setting.

space must be realised and allowed for around the principal lines of your design. Strong lines in the arrangement are emphasised if bare branches and tall pointed leaves are used. When arranged properly these should lead the eye on a precise path to the centre of the design.

An appropriate background is most important. If the walls are pale, dark branches and bright leaves and foliage will stand out dramatically, but if the background is dark, flowers of yellow, orange and scarlet will show up well.

The correct container is also important and should be plain and uncluttered in appearance. A modern container made from metal or pottery would be suitable.

Although flowers alone can make interesting modern designs, a contrast of form will make the pattern more eye-catching. For instance, a tall branch and a large leaf such as Fatsia with short flowers grouped low down, or tall flowers placed one below the other to form a vertical line with a piece of gnarled wood placed low in the design, will prove more exciting than six flowers all of one kind placed in an upright container.

So if you are interested in making creative modern arrangements, make a start by looking for accessories which would be useful for adding a different shape or form to your design. Collect some large stones, rough pieces of wood, old roots, shells and even ornaments which are all valuable accessories to modern flower arranging. Pieces of wood and bark can be used to obtain interesting textures, or the wood can be rubbed smooth and polished with shoe polish or painted with clear varnish. Bare branches can be painted in exciting colours and reels of cane, which can be purchased from craft shops, can make twists and curls to add to a design.

In making modern designs you establish the height first by inserting a branch or thin leaves or seed sprays into a pin-holder in the base of the container. There is little transition in a modern design so you can drop suddenly to a large leaf placed low down and perhaps spreading outwards. The arrangement can then be finished with large flowers or a cluster of smaller ones all of the same colour, tied together and placed at the base of the tallest stem to represent a colour block. In fact modern designs are stark, dramatic and exciting because of the strong use of colour. The final effect should be the exact opposite to a traditional formal design, where you use various sizes and shapes of flowers as transition to carry the eye from the outside to the centre of the composition.

Many students ask for the modern style to be defined more closely to assist them in their choice of plant material. So for those who wish to recognise this style more clearly the following list provides a few guidelines which are generally accepted.

Sharp contrasts	Sharp change of form
Few materials	Importance of space, even if enclosed
Clean linear pattern	Sudden changes of colour or form
Bold forms	Strong textures
Exotic material	Broad leaves
Intense colours	Curves against straight lines

Other Important Styles

Free style This is considered to be the next step after the Modern style, and it allows the arranger greater individuality since the style does not conform to any preconceived or accepted pattern. It may be thought that this gives you the freedom to do anything you like and in a way you can, but having studied the basics, even a free-style design conforms in some ways to the principles of design. For example, all the stems must rise from one point. However, in free style, flower arranging becomes an expressive art form. In this style you are released from the prescribed measurements and can create very tall arrangements, or use wire or circling branches for width to enclose a space. You can twist or knot the material and use any of the elements in an unconventional way. In fact, whether you place a large dried Allium head on top of a curved piece of cane, which continues its curl downwards over a heavy pottery jar, or make a black and white design using white painted dry leaves, or white flowers, and blackened wood, consider *yourself* to be the artist and continue to create.

Naturalistic (landscape) Originated by the Chinese, this is a most attractive style and is often seen at shows. It is particularly suitable for low coffee tables or a spot where an arrangement is easily noticed. It depicts a natural scene, such as a corner of a wood, the side of a stream, mountains, rocks, a lakeside, in fact any natural scene which has captured your imagination. Suitable plant material should be used to interpret your ideas, and if any accessory is used it should harmonise with your interpretation and also be in scale with the rest of the 'picture'.

Domes and pyramids These styles are ideal for a side table or a party table decoration. They do not take up a lot of room and are not easily knocked over. Press a dome of water-soaked floral foam onto a foam holder which has been secured to the top of a cake stand. Insert short-stemmed flowers into the foam so that the whole dome is covered with flowers. A taller cone can be used and filled in the same way with rings of flowers and greenery.

Cascade This is a very graceful style and is used in any stemmed type of vase or container, such as a goblet, a fruit stand or any container held aloft by a cherub or other ornament. Height should be given to the upper flowers as the flowers should flow downwards as though falling from a fountain. The longest stems should be at the sides and the central upright stem should be about half the length of the downward ones. Stems should also flow forwards and backwards. This style is suitable for delicate flowers.

Abstract (a) Decorative abstract is based only on design qualities and has no special theme; (b) expressive abstract is inspired by a definite theme and reflects the exhibitor's ideas on a particular subject, sometimes to the point of exaggeration.

In show work, various additional styles are introduced, such as Mobiles and Stabiles, which all bring me to realise that we have come a long way from the time when we considered an arrangement to be classified as 'a bowl of flowers for effect'. At that time it was never explained what effect was required. It seems today, with the increasing interest in the subject as an art form, that flower arranging is going in two directions: flowers for the home and flowers for shows. This all spells advancement in this fascinating subject.

Pot-et-Fleur

A *pot-et-fleur* is a design incorporating cut flowers with pot plants. The flowers and plants are grouped together, in or out of their pots, in a large container, perhaps a deep trough or a garden urn.

When selecting the plants make sure they will all survive under the same conditions, taking into consideration positioning, light, heat and watering. Prepare the container by first placing a layer of gravel in the bowl. This provides the plants with adequate drainage, as they hate to have their roots in water. If you place some charcoal on top of the gravel, this will help to keep the water pure. Sprinkle a little bone meal over the charcoal and gravel and then add a layer of potting compost.

Loosen the plants from their pots by pressing the sides of a plastic pot or gently tapping the sides of an earthenware pot. Place your hand over the top of the pot with the base of the plant supported between your middle fingers. Turn the pot upside down and the plant should fall smoothly into your hand with its soil still around its roots. Position the plants in the large container, placing the taller ones at the back or in the middle and the smaller ones at the front or around the sides. Trailing plants should always be near the edge of a container so they can trail down over the rim. Fill in between the plants, pressing the potting compost down firmly. Leave space to insert a tube, cone or small vase of water to hold the cut flowers.

Design

No grouping of any items can appear integrated or attractive without a feeling for design. So it is with plants, leaves and fruit. By placing the tallest and slenderest material, whether it be tall wood, fine green sprays or thin flowers, on the outside, and the bigger, more dominant items at the focus of attention at the base of the main stems, the eye is led from the outside or top of the design to the hub of interest, where the eye should rest. Design means the joining together of items of different size, form and colour into a unified whole, this co-ordination of stems or items being emphasised by dominant interest in the centre.

In foliage arrangements, dominant interest could be a group of variegated leaves; with fruit it could be the

brightest or most shiny piece; in plant arrangements it could be the plant with the largest leaves and in a flower arrangement it would be the largest, more attractive flowers. Stones and chunks of wood can also be items of dominant interest. The spot in the design where the dominant interest is placed is often described as the focal point, the heart or the hub of the design.

Transition

Items used in transition are those which take the eye from, for example, fine sprays to a broad leaf. They should soften the move from one item to another, and are placed between contrasts.

Imagine a painting in which a narrow path leads you to a red-roofed white cottage; here the cottage is the dominant interest or focal point, the path being the inviting touch which leads you from the outside of the picture to the heart of it. Yet the artist will have placed along the path a shrub, or a puddle, or a twist – any subtle change of emphasis that will break up the directness of the thin path to the solid cottage. So, when composing with plant material you need some 'in between' items as transition, except in abstract and some modern designs. These items should not be as strong as the strongest feature nor as noticeable as the highlights. They could be grey leaves to soften two strong colours, or an insignificant item to act as a buffer between two equally good items. You may be using bright fruit grouped at the base of driftwood, in which case a trail of mellowing vine leaves with ends twined about the fruit will soften the junction.

Scale

Scale means proportion. To scale one's decoration to fit the background in which it will be seen is to keep it in proportion with the other items in the room. It also means keeping the plant material in proportion with the container used, as well as scaling the plant items with each other. For instance, fine ferns or carrot leaves, although most decorative, would not appear happy placed with large broad Hosta leaves, neither would the fine leaves be ideally suited to a pottery container. Yet these same leaves would combine well with Plantain seed spikes in a glass container. A tall Rubber Plant will decorate a corner in a lofty room, whereas a grouping of *Begonia rex* leaves backed perhaps with a tall vine or Sansevieria would complement a setting in a panelled room with a low ceiling. A sitting-room decorated in pastel colours might be enhanced by trails of Ivy, ruffled ferns or Tradescantia or dainty flowers. So I advise you to think of your setting

31

when planning your plants and choose them in accordance with the background against which they will be seen.

Textures

Textures are important. A couturier will place a touch of silk or velvet against a dull surface to emphasise a particular line or aspect of his creation; and the plant arranger searches likewise for the contrasting textures that will produce most effect. A shiny leaf will add brilliance to a grouping of dull-surfaced leaves, just as the varnish-like finish of green peppers and aubergines will highlight a grouping of dull-surfaced fruits and vegetables, such as pears, artichokes and cucumbers with Swiss chard leaves. Certain leaves, such as heavier *Begonia rex* and Paeony, will supply depth and main interest in a design; while the finer trails, like Ivy, Rosemary or Artemisia, are more suitable for the outside of the arrangement.

I often place the large swerving leaves of the Onopordum Thistle on the outside of a large pedestal group, and in this you may argue that I am contradicting myself, for surely the flat surface of these large leaves should not be used as framework or outside material. I should explain that as these leaves are grey, they are visually light; they are also long, pointed and swerving and are in good scale for a large group. This means that if they are used on the outside, something much bolder and more dominant, such as large flowers, artichoke heads, onion seed-heads or their own thistle heads, should be used in the centre. Of course, it would look wrong if, after making the framework with these leaves, the centre was finished with delicate leaves or grasses, because the weight would then be in the wrong place. So do open your eyes to the textural value of different leaves and plants.

Composition

Every flower, leaf or plant arrangement is in itself a composition, and so many novices wonder how to begin. The secret of composing is to bring together a number of elements in a rhythmic movement that finishes on a pleasing note.

When setting out to make a composition, collect all your items and decide which of them shall be used for main interest, because everything you want to express with them cannot be of equal importance. Therefore, if you have picked onion seed-heads and artichoke heads for the centre, it would be better to eliminate one of them, just as you must decide between bright green peppers and pale yellow lemons for main interest in a grouping of fruit; the rest of the composition must be subordinate to one dominant interest only.

Of course, this will be much simpler if you can decide what you want before picking or buying. Suppose that, when looking for leaves in the garden, you find some flushed green Begonia leaves which you think will be ideal for central interest; you will then look for some different shapes to go behind them, finally searching for fine sprays for the outside. In a smaller garden you might find a twisted branch to give height to a modern design, and use the Begonia leaves for transition to your main interest, which could be apples, cones, or a piece of tree wood. So you will find composition easier if you look for the following items:

1. Tall fine outside material
2. Medium interest transition material
3. More interesting main items that are dominant in shape or colour.

The best flower arrangers study these principles until they are instinctive, and once they require no effort to bring them to mind, they can visualise a grouping round any living plant form almost at once. With plants in particular they will automatically 'see' that the tallest plant should be at the back and the trailing one at the side, with the broad-leafed one at the base of the tall one. It is this quick assessment of different forms, shapes and colours that simplifies the grouping of living plant material.

The Show Competitor

It is a natural move for many flower arrangers to progress from making flower arrangements in the home to entering a competition at a show. Many flower club members admit that they learn more from competing in a show than from any other practice, for by competing they try just that bit harder than they need to at home, and in this way they experiment a little more and see much more, which in turn extends their repertoire. Yet many fail when they first enter in a show and often cannot understand why. The most recurring reason is that the schedule has not been properly read and interpreted. For instance, in a class for 'fruit and leaves' you might add a few of your favourite flowers, just as you would at home. In such a case your exhibit would be disqualified, for the schedule did not ask for flowers, only 'fruit and leaves'. It is rather like entering your lovely poodle in a class at a dog show which asked for 'Scottish terriers'.

The first thing to do when trying your skills at a flower arrangement show is to *read the schedule carefully*. As a rule a lot of thought and work by the committee has gone into its production to make it interesting for competitors and the public, and if, as you read it, there are items you do not understand, it is advisable to telephone or write to the show secretary, who will explain. Whatever ruling he or she gives will also be passed to the judges, so that all are in accord on the day.

It is advisable to enter only those classes you feel confident you can complete, so do not choose too many, unless you are very experienced and can gauge the time needed to complete them all. Your best work will evolve if you have time on your hands – but if you are trying to complete a number of arrangements and working with one eye on the clock, your work is sure to become a little mechanical.

Do make a check on all your needs, taking extra materials in case of accidents. Items you will find necessary may include pin-holders, wire-netting, reel wire, conical tin tubes (for mass or pedestal groups), glass orchid tubes (for short flowers high in a design), adhesive clay, rubber rings (to prevent holders and fruit from slipping), Twistems (to steady heavy branches at the back of tall containers), flower scissors, mist spray to moisten the surrounds of your exhibit, toothpicks (for fruit) and a long-spouted watering can. Chrysal powder (to keep flowers living longer), adhesive tape, drawing pins or paper clips or a stapling gun (for drapes), boxes (on which to stand exhibits for extra lift) and floral foam (and a knife with which to cut it) may all be used. Pieces of strip lead may be needed to hang on the wire at the back if your arrangement is inclined to tilt forward, though it should not do this if properly constructed. Take a bucket of water and, of course, the necessary containers, bases, backgrounds (which should be wrapped round newspaper or on a roller to avoid creases) and accessories, to which will be added, on the day, all the flowers and plant material.

Plan your arrangements well in advance. You cannot always decide upon the flowers you might use, for the weather and market fluctuations will have to be considered; but you can make a rough sketch of the sizes and shapes of flowers you will need to enable you to create the design you have decided upon.

Getting your plant material to the showground in a good state is important. There are many methods of doing this, depending upon the length and method of your journey. However, after conditioning your flowers and other plants, it has been found excellent for long journeys to pack everything in a plastic-lined flower box, close together to stop them moving about. Tissue paper

Staged against a dark blue background, the colouring and upward thrust of the flowers perfectly illustrate the title of the class, 'Flames upon a Midnight Sky'. Note the hand-made figurines placed low on the right as if running from the flames.

can be slid around precious blooms. Place long leaves at the bottom followed by the tall flowers, then place the shorter flowers and any shorter leaves on top of the tall stems. Pack special blooms in a plastic bag. Cover the box with more plastic sheeting and tie it down. Place the flowers in a bucket of water on arrival at the show and give them a deep drink.

Another method, better for shorter journeys, is to place most flowers in a polythene bucket containing a little water, then pull a plastic bag over the heads of the blooms, tying this down firmly to the bucket to avoid loss of moisture. Fill the bucket with water on arrival to give the flowers a long deep drink. (See Conditioning and Care of Cut Flowers on page 12).

SHOW DEFINITIONS

The meaning of certain words, phrases and regulations in show work often proves difficult for the newcomer to understand, although today schedules are much more simply constructed than in the past. If the schedule states that 'any natural plant material may be used' it means any dry or fresh plant material, for dry is not artificial. If the title of the class is given and the words 'an exhibit' is all that is used, it means you should interpret the title. If there is any stipulation as to what can or cannot be used it is usually added as a condition.

Show definitions can usually be obtained from the show organisers but here is a list of the terms which have been in use for a number of years.

Accessory Any item, such as a plate, ornament, book etc., which is used in addition to the main flower arrangement. Stones, shells, marble and similar non-plant material are considered to be accessories, unless otherwise stated in the schedule.

Annual A flower or a plant that completes its cycle of growth in one year. A hardy annual is grown entirely out of doors.

Arrangement The artistic use of plant material, with or without accessories, in any stated or unstated container, with or without a base. (In N.A.F.A.S. shows this word is now superseded by the word 'exhibit'.)

Artificial Artificial, plastic or dyed flowers are not allowed in competitions unless the schedule states otherwise, for example, at Christmas time.

Background This is placed behind the exhibit and should be complementary to it. It can be made of any material.

Base An item on which a container can be stood, for example, wood, metal, fabric, china, plastic, slate, etc.

Basket A basket can have a handle or lid and should be made of any natural woven material, unless the schedule states otherwise.

Best in the show An award given to the best of all the first prize-winning exhibits, excluding collages and plaques.

Biennial A flower or plant which completes its growth in two years.

Bloom One flower or opened bud borne on a single stem, for example, Carnation, Dahlia, Tulip, Scabious.

Bowl A receptacle having a wide opening, the top diameter of which is greater than or equal to the height. It must rest on the table or be raised by a base not more than one-third its own height. The word is now almost obsolete.

Bud An unopened bloom not showing colour.

Candle This is considered an accessory, unless otherwise stated. Often used for colour and height in certain designs.

Catkins Hazel catkins are collections of the male flowers of the catkin.

Cluster Several fruits, berries or flowers growing close together on one stem, for example, currants, tomatoes, grapes, Phlox and climbing Roses.

Condition The actual quality of the plant material at the time of judging.

Container A receptacle in which flowers are exhibited. It can be made of any material and be of any texture, colour, shape or design which will enhance the beauty of the plant material arranged therein.

Contemporary Existing as of today.

Contrast A set of two things juxtaposed to accentuate their differences. To show a striking difference by comparison.

Design An overall plan which is made pleasing by the combination of all items used. It includes balance, rhythm and scale.

Distinction Something out of the ordinary yet not bizarre; notable for creative use of plant material.

Dominant This term in flower arrangement means something eye-catching, strong, influential, outstanding and over-looking other items.

Dried plant material This includes any dried, preserved, pressed or skeletonised natural plant material; also dried fruits, seed-heads, nuts, cones, grasses or sedges, in fact anything which at the time of use is not living. Generally this does not include painted or dyed flowers or the use of artificial material.

Driftwood A wide term used to describe wood which has been weathered by any of the natural elements, i.e., air, earth, fire or water, or that which is dead, dried, stripped, sand-blasted or polished.

Exotic When referring to plants, this means introduced from hot countries and nurtured in Britain in greenhouses. Many now grow happily outside, but the term 'exotic' generally refers to greenhouse plant material, and not outdoor-grown garden material.

Floral A term used to cover arrangements including all kinds of vegetable matter.

Floret A singly formed flower which is one of many on a spike, as found on Delphiniums, Gladioli, Acanthus, Phlox, Lilac, etc.

Flowers When a class refers to the use of a certain number of flowers it means blooms or opened buds borne on a single stem, such as Carnations and Tulips. A spike, such as a Gladiolus, is now included in this definition.

Focal point This refers to the heart of interest in a design; the point where all stems unite, usually found at the base of the tallest or main stems.

Foliage The leafage of a plant. Succulents and some bracts come under this heading. The term also refers to stems bearing leaves. A class for 'all foliage' can be of any colour.

Forced A term used to describe plants brought forward. This is often achieved with heat under glass to produce blooms out of season.

Formal A conventional arrangement, which is regular and symmetrical, in a suitable container.

Fragrance A quantity of odour which can be appreciated. Used in some classes, particularly those for the blind.

Fruit In horticultural terms this usually means the nuts, berries, seed-heads, gourds and cones of fruiting plants. Generally, whatever develops from a flower is a fruit. In flower arrangement shows, however, edible fruits, such as apples, pears, peaches, cherries, bananas and grapes, are also included.

Genus Botanically, this means a group of plants with common characteristics, such as Dianthus, which contains all the Pinks and Carnations. The plural of genus is genera.

Grasses Since it is difficult to distinguish when grass is in seed or flower the words 'grasses can be included' are added to schedules if they are needed. If 'any plant material' is stated, this would of course include grass.

Hardy flowers All flowers, whether grown from bulbs, corms, or herbaceous plants, which are grown entirely in the open.

Harmony This means that no one part of a design is developed at the expense of another, with all elements fitting together without jarring; a unity, a consistency of likeness.

Highlight A fine touch, a light note, a light-coloured flower, leaf or grass which attracts the eye before other features in a composition.

Holder A device for holding material in position in a container.

Incorporate This means to include – for example, certain items in a design.

Informal A casual type of arrangement – not conventional – using a simple type of container.

Kind This applies to separate genera such as Roses, Chrysanthemums and Zinnias, for example, 'using any kind of Rose'.

Landscape An exhibit portraying a natural scene.

Lichen This is considered natural plant material.

Line In flower arrangement this means showing strong linear pattern or outline, using a minimum of plant material so that line is not obscured.

Mass Massed overall design, using plenty of plant material and showing no clear-cut linear shape.

Miniature Up to 10 cm (4 inches) is the usual overall size for a miniature arrangement. Fundamental rules of design prevail, but scale is of great importance. Tiny flowers, grasses and leaves should be used so that if magnified ten times the whole would still be in proportion. Overall size includes vase and base.

Mobile An exhibit which hangs and moves in space.

Modern Modern designs are recognised by clear-cut plant forms and bold colouring. Contrast of textures is a distinguishing feature. Dramatic lines are used to contrast or blend with modern décor.

Moribana A Japanese style of arrangement in a shallow container.

Nageire A Japanese free or 'thrown-in' style of arrangement in an upright vase.

Natural plant material Fresh and/or dried plant material.

Neutral Grey is considered a neutral in flower colour classes. Pewter vases have a neutralising effect.

Niche A space backed with cardboard, wood or other material to form a recess in which an exhibit is placed.

Originality Recognised as the verve with which unusual plant material is used. An unusual vase, colour or style can produce originality.

Perennial A flower or plant that lives, blooms and sets seeds for more than two years.

Period When exhibitors are asked to portray a particular period, such as Victorian, Georgian, *avant-garde* or modern, flowers illustrative of the period should be used as near as possible.

Petite An exhibit more than 10 cm (4 inches) and less than 23 cm (9 inches) overall.

Predominate In classes where one colour or one kind of flower must predominate, this means that the particular colour or flower must be the stronger or be superior in quantity to the rest of the materials used.

Proportion The relationship of one part of an arrangement to another, be it flowers to each other, flowers to container or the whole to background. An arrangement 30 cm (12 inches) high would be out of proportion in a 1 metre (3 foot) niche as there would be too much empty space at the top.

Recess To recess a flower or leaf is to place it more deeply into the inside of the arrangement, to contrast with another which might protrude, thus giving an 'in and out' uneven effect.

Rhythm Rhythm in a flower arrangement is usually created by the use of graduated sizes, repetition and transition without monotony, to give movement.

Sea fern, Sea fan and Coral These are animal and not plant material.

Seaweed This is plant material.

Sedges Grass-like plants which grow in marshes or by the waterside.

Space Whether a niche is provided or not, this means the given space in which an arrangement must be placed. No exhibit should extend the given space or touch the sides of a niche.

Species A plant form found in nature – not produced by man, as is a hybrid.

Spike A term applied to a flower structure with short-stemmed flowers attached to a single unbranched stem, for example, Gladiolus, Delphinium.

Spray A part of a plant or shrub bearing a number of flowers on one stem, for example, Solidago, Forsythia and some Chrysanthemums.

Stabile A mobile suspended from a stand which is stable.

Still–life An arrangement with other objects, such as fruit, books and upturned pottery, designed to make a composition or picture.

Subservient A term used to describe an item less important than the others in a flower composition. This item is useful as a means of relating one thing to another, but plays no important part.

Table decoration An exhibit, with or without accessories, to be viewed 'all round'.

Texture The tissue structure of plant material may be smooth or rough, dull or glossy, fine or heavy.

Transition The change or passage from one item to another in a flower arrangement, often gradual in a mass style. Good transition can give movement in a curved style.

Variations The word 'variations' allows for the use of tints and shades of one colour and its adjacent colours (see colour wheel this page).

Variegated A term used to describe plants marked with irregular patches of a contrasting colour, mostly applied to leaves bearing decorative markings of white, cream or yellow.

Variety A particular form of a species or hybrid, such as *Achillea filipendulina* 'Gold Plate'. *Achillea* is the name of the genus, *filipendulina* the species, and 'Gold Plate' the particular variety.

Vase A container which is taller than the diameter of the opening at the top. A word now being superseded by 'container'.

Water Do not forget to put it in your container.

Wire Wire-netting used as a support should not show. Wiring of stems is not allowed.

X is for Xeranthemum, a hardy annual with everlasting composite flowers.

Y is for you and your good efforts, which are required at every show.

Z is for zeal used in advancing the cause of good flower shows.

COLOUR DEFINITIONS

Colour appeals to our senses whether at home or at a show. You need gay and bright colours at home for a cocktail party and possibly quiet colours for an intimate dinner. However, at shows you should use the colours that will help you interpret the title of the class. For instance, if entering in a class for a 'Seascape' it would be preferable if you used blue, grey and perhaps mauve, which are all receding colours which portray distance and the sea. Alternatively, if interpreting a war-like class, you would use fiery reds with suitable accessories. Do remember that accessories should be in keeping with the theme, not only in size but also in spirit, giving atmosphere. Plant material must always predominate.

However, as some terminology is needed before colour can be discussed, you may find it helpful to study the colour wheel below, and the colour guide on page 38.

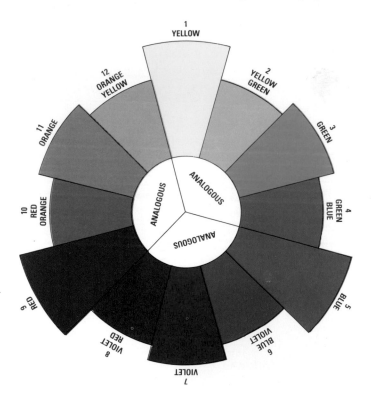

ABOVE: *The colour wheel (see page 38).*

OPPOSITE: *The flame-coloured Lilies, the lighter coloured single Chrysanthemums, and the olive green sprays of Eucalyptus leaves harmonise with the décor of this room. The flowers were inserted into two blocks of water-soaked floral foam which were held together by a stick pushed down through the centre into a pin-holder in the base of the container.*

THE FLOWER ARRANGER'S COLOUR GUIDE

Primary colours	Secondary colours	Tertiary colours	
red	green	yellow-green	violet-red
yellow	violet	blue-green	red-orange
blue	orange	blue-violet	orange-yellow

Advancing or warm colours	Receding or cool colours
(9–12 on colour wheel)	(2–5 on colour wheel)
red	yellow-green
red-orange	green
orange	green-blue
orange-yellow	blue

Analogous or adjacent colours	Complementary colours (opposites)
(1–4 on colour wheel)	(1 and 7 or 5 and 11 on colour wheel)
yellow	yellow/violet
yellow-green	blue/orange
green	green/red
green-blue	
(or 9–12 on colour wheel)	
red	
red-orange	
orange	
orange-yellow	

Split complementary colours	Monochromatic harmony
These are one colour and two adjacent to its complement, e.g., 1, 6 and 8 on colour wheel	The tints and shades of any one colour
yellow	
blue-violet	
violet-red	

Hue: The name of a colour, e.g., a hue of red

Triadic

Shade: A darker version of a colour

Tint: A lighter version of a colour

Tone: A greyed version of a colour

Three colours equidistant on the colour wheel, e.g., 2, 6 and 10   or 3, 7 and 11

yellow-green	green
blue-violet	violet
red-orange	orange

Using Colour

Of course these definitions are for the more serious student who might be asked to stage an arrangement using complementary colours or to interpret a show class entitled 'The coming of spring using analogous (adjacent) colours'. The flower arranger at home need not know about these principles, although some understanding of colour and its effect is often very useful.

Blue, although a lovely colour, does not show up under artificial light, nor in dark interiors such as a church. I once saw some beautiful blue Delphiniums arranged in a canvas tent for a wedding reception. The effect was depressing for it was a dull day outside and no light penetrated the tent to give these stately flowers a lift. They need a spotlight or to be mixed generously with other light flowers. Yet blue gives an atmosphere of coolness during the day and, mixed with other flowers, it gives a lovely effect in a light sunny room or on a patio.

Green is another cool colour. It tones down other colours near to it, so if you want a brilliant colour arrangement, do not use too much foliage. On the other hand, there is nothing more beautiful than a group of mixed greens. Placed on a dining table with perhaps some fruit added, it is an ideal colour.

Yellow is bright and gay; it immediately lifts the spirit and is an ideal choice to use after the long winter months. There are flowers of various tints and shades of yellow, which when placed together with young acid green foliage make a striking combination.

Red flowers are ideal for really rich arrangements. All variations of red appear magnificent in a large group, and, if you wish to make it even more effective, omit green leaves and use mainly maroon foliage such as *Berberis thunbergii atropurpurea*, *Prunus ceracifera* 'Pissardii', *Rosa rubrifolia* or even Beetroot from the kitchen garden.

Pastel colours are ideal for choice settings and they often express the character of the one who uses them. Almost like the inside of some shells or the effect of the semiprecious opals, the soft pinks and lavenders, mauves, pale blues and creams create a delicate atmosphere which never fails to please. Such pastel-coloured flowers might, on the other hand, be missed at a bright noisy cocktail party, when more harsh or stronger colours would be a better choice.

Tawny browns are good against a highly coloured background but they look their best when heightened with orange-coloured additions.

Pink is ideal for a young girls' gathering or can be mixed with other toning colours for table centres or side tables; although it is hardly strong enough to be the focal interest in a large room.

White is cooling in summer and an all-white arrangement with lime green leaves or the lovely Lady's Mantle (*Alchemilla mollis*) can make an unforgettable arrangement. Used often at weddings for its symbolism of purity, it is a little cold to use in winter.

However, the choice is yours. You may prefer mixed colours. Some like to be guided, others know what they like, but luckily the whole of the colour spectrum can be found in flowers.

HINTS FOR JUDGES

The six main principles used in judging flower arrangements are:

> Interpretation of the schedule
> Design, which includes balance and scale
> Colour, to interpret the class title
> Suitability of container and flowers
> Condition of plant material
> Distinction and originality.

Make sure that the exhibit interprets the title of the class, not only in the idea and its presentation but also in colour. See that accessories, if used, are in keeping in spirit and size with the main arrangement and that everything is in prime condition. Check that no wire or floral foam is showing and that the back of the design is not flat. It is generally accepted that plant material should predominate in all exhibits, so study this item, and make sure that vases, bases and any materials used are in perfect condition. If title cards are required, assess the style of writing and presentation of these cards.

If, as a judge, you are asked to write a comment card, do try to write a good point first as encouragement, then very clearly and concisely add an instructive note if you can.

Most women's organisations, such as the National Association of Flower Arrangement Societies, the National Federation of Women's Institutes and the National Union of Townswomen's Guilds, have their own schedule definitions and guides, and all judges should accede to the organisers' wishes. A good judge should not be influenced by any remark passed by a member of the committee or a steward, and the whole experience will be more enjoyable if he or she tries to develop the following qualities: knowledge, experience, impartiality, courage, tact and fairness.

FLOWERS
IN THE HOME

Flowers bring a home to life – whether they form a brightly coloured group in the hall to greet friends or a pastel-coloured posy in the bedroom to charm a guest, they will never go unnoticed. Finding new ways of using flowers to complement different room settings offers you an exciting opportunity to project your own personality through the creative use of colour or an individual style of arrangement. However you use your flowers, always put a little of your heart and personal style into arranging them. Even informal flowers in kitchens or bathrooms will give more pleasure if care is taken over the selection of the flowers and the choice of the container. It is worth remembering that it is not only your own enjoyment in arranging flowers that is important, but the great uplift you give to others who see them.

Informal Arrangements

Informality means not striving for effect, but allowing the flowers to look natural and true-to-life in their container. There are no fixed rules and the arrangement may not consist of a studied colour scheme, or, indeed, any particular design. A perfect informal arrangement need not rely on the use of mechanics and the flowers should support each other with the help of the edges of the container. This is not always possible and the choice is left very much to the individual. Whether the arrangement consists of a mixed bunch of flowers from the garden or is the result of picking bits and pieces from the hedgerows, the casualness and air of simplicity adds delightful charm to any home.

At the same time, what may appear informal in one home may not be so in another. For instance, a bunch of Marigolds set in a pewter tankard would appear informal and very acceptable in many settings but would not look so lovely if set on a fine antique table in an elegant period house. So, although there are no set rules, the surroundings and background of an informal arrangement must be taken into account.

Containers for informal arrangements should be simple and basic but must still unite with the flowers. All kinds of kitchen utensils, such as storage jars, kitchen scales, copper kettles and saucepans can be used. Glass food containers and vases are excellent as they can be found in a wide variety of simple shapes and sizes. Stone pickling jars and cider bottles are ideal for bunches of flowers. Loosely tie three or four bunches together, pulling up some flowers so that all the heads are not standing together. Insert these into the jar so that the heads come just above the rim. Such a colour-block of flowers placed in a tubular-shaped container looks most attractive when placed under a table lamp. A wine glass painted with iridescent nail varnish or car spray paint and then filled with dainty pink flowers, such as Pinks, is an eye-catching arrangement. Cups and saucers can make interesting containers and wine bottles are a never-ending source of delight. Stand a wine bottle in a wine cooler, insert a candle into the top of the bottle and fill the cooler with short-stemmed flowers for an unusual display. It is these little effects and changing ideas which give such satisfaction, so open your eyes and try something different.

Pieces of driftwood, or 'found wood' as it is called today, are a useful adjunct to informal arrangements. Try inserting a tall twisted branch into a pin-holder in a shallow dish, to give height, then add some casual flowers lower down, finishing with a chunk of wood or some stones to cover the holder. Wood can be introduced into many informal arrangements, so keep your eyes open when walking in the woods, the countryside or by rivers or the seashore; all kinds of treasures can be found and you will be surprised at the exciting 'pictures' which can be made from combining flowers and natural flora. A piece of grey-coloured wood, found on the bank of a river or lake can be placed on a black base with a bunch of colourful Anemones peeping from behind, making not only an interesting 'picture' but a reminder of the place where the wood was found.

Many pieces of wood can be made to stand without added support by sawing the base evenly. Others will need the addition of a short dowel stick, which can be inserted at the required angle into the piece of wood. This is done by drilling a hole in the wood and gluing one end of the dowel into it. The other end of the dowel can be inserted into a hole which has been drilled into a wooden base. A tall curved branch of wood, such as stripped Ivy,

to remove any dead material or debris, they are either varnished or rubbed over with furniture or shoe polish. The latter will give various coloured surfaces. If you do not want to conceal the texture of the wood by heavy varnish, try brushing the wood with a mixture made from one cup of clear ammonia, two tablespoons of copper powder (obtained from art or hardware shops), and two or three tablespoons of white glue. This gives an interesting effect as the mixture will oxidise and after it has dried it will assume a lovely blue-green patina which emphasises the texture of the wood.

A few years ago we would not have dreamt of using wood with flowers in the home, but today flower arranging has reached such a high pitch of artistry that any natural plant material (and wood is just that) is used to add form or shape or colour to floral decorations. Yet wood is not suitable for every setting. An attractive grouping can be made by incorporating flowers with a treasured ornament. Many ornaments are either tucked away in a cupboard or are taken for granted since they are always there to be seen in the same position on a shelf or table. Try standing the ornament on a base and behind it place a well-holder filled with a few casual flowers. This will not only bring the ornament into greater prominence, but will make the arrangement much more effective.

Flowers for everyday use need not be so studied as those for special occasions, yet your imagination can be given full play as you look around the home. A pair of kitchen scales can have flowers placed on one side and be balanced on the other side with various fruits. If, however,

can be held in place by simply screwing a flat piece of wood onto the base of the branch. This flat base can be placed in a container and covered with stones, moss or small plants.

Writing of stripped Ivy, I am often asked how this can be prepared. Use the curved pieces of the Ivy that grows up the bark of trees in woods. Few people mind this being removed as it will eventually kill the host tree if left. After picking the Ivy rub off any dead leaves until only the stem remains, then soak it in a bath of hot, strong, washing soda and water overnight (a handful of soda with enough water to cover the Ivy). The next morning you should be able to rub or scrape off the bark, leaving a white shiny surface. After removing all the bark (more soaking may be needed if this proves difficult), place the Ivy branch in a solution of water and household bleach (one dessertspoon to one pint). This will prevent the branch from turning yellow. Rinse the branch well in clear water before allowing it to dry. If you have picked the Ivy at random and not selected a definite shape or size of branch for your design, you can screw, nail or glue pieces together. If you wish to make a really exciting modern design, the branch can be spray painted any colour you wish. Red Carnations and black painted wood make an exciting display, so do not hesitate to try different colours for a modern setting.

Some chunky pieces of wood give the atmosphere of a country setting when they are combined with wild flowers – Daisies, Marigolds or any unsophisticated flowers usually evoke interest. On the other hand, many interesting shapes of 'found wood' can be made to appear less rural if, after they have first been brushed with a stiff brush

43

your scales are of the modern type a casual arrangement of flowers and foliage can be placed in the weighing tray.

It is not only in living rooms, dining rooms and entrance halls that flower arrangements are appropriate. With the trend towards country kitchens it is very acceptable to have flowers or foliage on display. These must fit in with the general décor and style of the kitchen and be placed so as not to interfere with the preparation of food.

A large jug filled with stalks of corn, barley and deep blue Cornflowers or a few Poppies, of which there are a wide range to choose from, will make a suitable arrangement. Poppies make a beautiful informal arrangement on their own. Iceland Poppies are the best variety for cut flowers and their tissue-paper-like textured flowers are borne on leafless stems. They come in a variety of different colours, ranging through a mixture of red, pink, orange and yellow. Their stem ends must be sealed in the flame of a match or in boiling water if they are to last. It is also best to pick them when they are in bud, but make sure some colour is showing as all-green buds will not open once they are cut.

A bunch of all-white flowers placed in a simple white china container is suitable for a country kitchen as well as an austere modern formica one. Simple flowers, such as Daisies, Marguerites (*Chrysanthemum frutescens*) or Ox-eye Daisies (*Chrysanthemum leucanthemum*) are all ideal.

Bathrooms can also look most attractive with flower arrangements in them. A carefully placed posy of flowers or some colourful plants arranged along a windowsill can make all the difference to this room, which can often look rather cold. The arrangements can be either dried or fresh flowers. Pampas Grasses placed in a tall container standing on the floor can make a long-lasting display, which will look especially fine in a dark bathroom as the fluffy pale-coloured plumes will stand out against a dark back-

OPPOSITE: *Dainty flowers, such as Freesias and Heather, grouped in a shell-like container make a charming and sweet-smelling posy for a bedroom.*
BELOW: *For this hall table arrangement, a shallow dish was filled with water-soaked floral foam pressed onto a pin-holder to give stability. Short flowers and leaves were used, working from the outside towards the centre.*

ground. Flowers placed in front of a mirror or mirror tiling will have to be arranged symmetrically as they will be reflected in the mirror. A single rose or bloom can be placed in a long-stemmed container for the side of a wash basin or shelf. Groups of potted plants also look very effective in bathrooms and most varieties will thrive in the warm and humid atmosphere.

Bedroom flower arrangements should blend in with the decoration of the room and must be placed so that they cannot be knocked over in the dark. Peaceful flowers are suitable for most bedrooms, so make good use of pastel-shaded flowers. Sweet Peas, Foxgloves (sometimes called the Wader flower or Angel's Fishing Rod with its arching stems of speckled trumpet-shaped flowers), Freesias or delicately coloured Irises such as 'Blue Denim', are all suitable. These can be placed on windowsills, bedside tables or dressing tables.

INFORMAL TABLE ARRANGEMENTS

For everyday informal table arrangements, freedom of expression is the keynote. Wild flowers, Daisies, Marigolds, Gaillardias (sometimes known as the Blanket flower), gold and bronze Heleniums, Sunflowers, wheat and grasses are all ideal when placed in pottery jars or casserole dishes on a scrubbed wooden kitchen table. For family gatherings it is nice to place a coloured cloth on the table and place an arrangement consisting of all the same type of flower. A massed bowl of crimson Godetias, set on a green cloth can appear very effective, or orange-coloured Dahlias, placed casually on a brown cloth. Paper napkins can contrast or match. Cloths or sheets can

45

always be cold water dyed to any colour, offering a wide variety of flowers to choose from for the centre or off-centre table arrangement.

Candles will not only cut down the cost of flowers but make an enchanting decoration for a candle-light supper. A tall green candle can be inserted into a block of floral foam which has been placed in a dish of water. The foam can be covered with green leaves to surround the base of the candle. Alternatively, secure a candlestick on a 5 cm (2 inch) piece of floral foam and stand this on a dessert plate. Then arrange small flowers into the foam to cover it and make the candlestick look as if it is standing on a dome of flowers.

For a very simple but effective arrangement, try placing Daisies between fruit in a bowl. Another idea is to fill a clear glass bottle with water (to which a few drops of food colouring or coloured ink have been added), and arrange a few flowers of a similar colour in the top. A large brandy glass filled with small shells into which a few flowers have been inserted makes another interesting informal table design.

The idea is to ring the changes as the seasons change, and just as you would vary the menu to stimulate the appetite of your family and friends, so also will their interest be aroused by a change of table setting.

WILD FLOWER ARRANGEMENTS

There is a certain fascination about wild flowers and grasses which never ceases to appeal. Perhaps it is their old-world charm which allows them to be appreciated in any setting, for they seem just as at home in a sophisticated setting as they do in a country cottage. Their very casualness is enchanting in whichever room of the house they are placed.

Wild flowers abound all over the world, but there are laws to protect them from indiscriminate picking. This does not mean that wild flowers cannot be picked, but certain plants must not be dug up without permission. Remember wild flowers are there for everyone's enjoyment, so do not pick more than you need.

No-one would object to the picking of Rosebay Willowherb (*Epilobium angustifolium*) with its 90 cm (3 feet) tall stems of heavy rose-coloured flowers, as it grows in profusion on waste ground, heaths and wood clearings from June through to September. When this flower goes to seed the wind carries the tiny seeds to other areas where they set and grow. The stems of the seed-pods before and even after they have burst are very attractive, and can be used in autumnal and dry flower arrangements.

There is a wealth of flowers to be found in the Wild Carrot family, many of which grow in the hedgerows and along the verges of roads. There is white Goutweed (*Aegopodium podagraria*) and Hemlock (*Conium maculatum*), and the Wild Carrot (*Daucus carota*), not forgetting the white Cow Parsley (*Anthriscus sylvestris*) and Hogweed (*Heracleum sphondylium*), which is a must for large dry flower arrangements once it has gone to seed. Many of us are familiar with the Common Toadflax (*Linaria vulgaris*) with its yellow snapdragon-like flowers and tall 30–60 cm (1–2 feet) high spikes. This flower looks particularly delightful in a young child's bedroom. The Common Ragwort (*Senecio jacobaea*) grows along the roadsides and in fields and its yellow daisy-like flowers can be grouped together in one arrangement or used with other coloured flowers. Stems of Dock (*Rumex obtusifolius*) or Common Sorrel (*Rumex acetosa*), whether fresh or dry, are useful to all flower arrangers, but it is often the smaller plants such as Crosswort (*Galium cruciata*) and Lady's Bedstraw (*Galium verum*), with its strong honeyed scent, which are most useful for placing on a small side table.

Wild flowers seem more at home when casually arranged in simple containers or baskets. Yet I have seen some really attractive designs at shows which are made with wild flowers. However, at home they have a particular appeal when placed in clusters or bunches where some of their botanical imperfections do not offend the eye of the horticulturist.

Some people complain that cut wild flowers do not last; but of course they will last if they are treated correctly as soon as they are picked. Remember that once the flower has been deprived of its natural source of nourishment it will quickly go limp. To avoid this, the flowers should be guarded from wind and warm air and placed in water directly they are gathered. In their natural habitat the flowers replace the moisture they lose due to the wind and sun, by drawing moisture up through their roots and up their stem to the flower. This cannot happen once they are picked, but if they are wrapped in wet newspaper so that it covers their heads as well as stems, or, alternatively, placed in a large polythene bag which is then tied at the top, this will help them to keep their moisture during the journey home. Once at home it is best to re-cut the stems and plunge them into a deep jug or bucket of water. Leave them in a cool place for some hours or overnight if possible. Any big stems should be cut slantwise, otherwise if they rest flat on the bottom of the receptacle they cannot absorb so much water.

Also all large flat leaves and leafy twigs should be completely submerged in water. The next morning the stems and leaves should be straight and strong. This is because they are full of moisture and they should last much longer in your decoration.

Plan your design and colour scheme with wild flowers just as you would if you were using garden flowers. Do not fall into the habit of picking everything you see in the hedgerows or woods, but try to have an idea in your mind when you are looking for foliage and flowers and pick only the ones you need.

Imagine what a pretty arrangement could be made in the summer by using some sprays of green Dock at the back for height and then placing lovely heads of white Cow Parsley or Queen Anne's Lace lower down. Quite near the rim of the container you could insert green leaves, perhaps of Plantain and in between a few wild Common Toadflax. This would look very attractive placed in a basket and could be left *in situ* to dry.

Another charming summer decoration could be made with wild Foxgloves or delightful tall sprays of Rosebay Willowherb. Both of these pink-shaded flowers could be used for background height in a large arrangement. If you combine these with a few purple Spear Thistles (*Cirsium vulgare*), some pale mauve Field Scabious (*Knautia arvensis*) and perhaps blooms of Red Clover (*Trifolium pratense*) and Wild Heather, you would have a beautifully harmonious colour scheme. This scheme might only be improved by adding a tiny touch of some yellow flowers near to the centre. The idea of adding an unobtrusive touch of yellow to an otherwise monotone arrangement will often lift it and give it life, but try it first

and see if you like the effect. If you don't, leave it out, for you are the one who makes the final decision.

Wild grasses alone make an effective decoration which will last all through the winter. Try arranging them with some of the dry flowers, such as the dainty pink straw-textured everlasting *Helipterum roseum* or the yellow-centred red or white flowers of *Helipterum manglesii*.

Honeysuckle, too, can be enchanting as a side-table decoration, especially if you allow some of the tendrils to trail over the rim of the container. This delicate flower will also fill the air with its unforgettable perfume.

Protected Wild Flowers

Here is a list of wild flowers and plants which are protected under the 1975 Act for the Conservation of Wild Creatures and Wild Plants.

Common name	Botanical name
Alpine Gentian	*Gentiana nivalis*
Alpine Sow-thistle	*Cicerbita alpina*
Alpine Woodsia	*Woodsia alpina*
Blue Heath	*Phyllodoce caerulea*
Cheddar Pink	*Dianthus gratianopolitanus*
Diapensia	*Diapensia lapponica*
Drooping Saxifrage	*Saxifraga cernua*
Ghost Orchid	*Epipogium aphyllum*
Killarney Fern	*Trichomanes speciosum*
Lady's-slipper	*Cypripedium calceolus*
Mezereon	*Daphne mezereum*
Military Orchid	*Orchis militaris*
Monkey Orchid	*Orchis simia*
Oblong Woodsia	*Woodsia ilvensis*
Red Helleborine	*Cephalanthera rubra*
Snowdon Lily	*Lloydia serotina*
Spiked Speedwell	*Veronica spicata*
Spring Gentian	*Gentiana verna*
Teesdale Sandwort	*Minuartia stricta*
Tufted Saxifrage	*Saxifraga cespitosa*
Wild Gladiolus	*Gladiolus illyricus*

Special Occasions

Whatever the special event is, whether it is a birthday, a wedding, a christening, an anniversary, Easter, Guy Fawkes, Hallowe'en or St Valentine's Day, it offers a marvellous chance to show skill and expression with flowers. In eastern and southern lands especially, flowers have for centuries been employed as a medium for conveying romantic feelings. The myriad lovers of Turkey, Persia and Greece were singularly ingenious in the art of conversation in the language of flowers. Flowers still have the same meanings as then, and by studying the following list, you may find some flowers which will fit in with some of the special occasions we are called upon to celebrate from time to time.

Acacia (white): Friendship.

Achillea ptarmica: A double flowering Yarrow meaning 'seven years of love' and often carried by country bridesmaids to signify a long union of the bridal couple.

Aconite: Lustre or Gold-shining.

Agrimony: Thankfulness.

Flowering Almond: Hope.

Ambrosia: Love Returned.

Aster ('China'): Variety is Charming.

Barley: Plenty.

Beech tree: Prosperity.

Cow Parsley: Festivity.

Euphorbia: Good Nourishment.

Flowering Rush: Music.

Forget-me-not: True Love.

Honeysuckle: Rustic Beauty.

Ivy: Friendship.

Lady's mantle: Dearly valued.

White Lilac: Youthful Innocence.

Lily of the Valley: Return of Happiness.

Myrtle: Love. This was often included in Victorian bridal bouquets.

Pink (single): Pure Love.

Rose: Love.

Rosemary: Remembrance.

Snowball or Guelder Rose: Winter.

Dwarf Sunflower: Adoration. Clytie dying of unrequited love was changed by Apollo into a Sunflower, which always turns towards the sun.

A mass of flowers all of one colour is often more effective than a mixture.

Tulip: Declaration of Love. In the East the flaming petals represent the wooer's glowing cheeks and the black centre his heart 'burned up with passion'.

Water-Lily: Purity of Heart.

Wood Sorrel: Joy.

Zinnia: Thoughts of Absent Friends.

FLOWERS FOR PARTIES

Whenever there is a special celebration, let the flowers help tell the story; play up the theme, even if you have to suppress some of your personal likes. This means that even if you are fond of pink Chrysanthemums placed on beautiful lace cloths, there are certain parties where these would be totally unsuitable. Choose the flowers to fit the occasion.

Guy Fawkes' and Autumn Parties

Guy Fawkes' night is mainly celebrated by children but as the event must be supervised by adults a few suitable flower arrangements in the house will be appreciated. These arrangements can feature erect Bulrushes to represent rockets (spray them with hair lacquer to prevent them from bursting open and spreading their fluffy seeds around the house). Some of them can be sprayed with glitter-paint to resemble sparklers and placed as the background to a grouping of flame-red Nerines and gold and yellow Chrysanthemums balanced low down with pieces of barkwood, twigs and other suitable items.

A festival of harvest is another occasion for which many parties are given. Most hostesses love this theme for it allows plenty of opportunity to display in abundance the fruits of the autumn garden and fields. Bright coloured flowers, fruit, berries, vegetables, grasses, wheat and barley can all be featured in arrangements. This plant material usually appears more effective when placed in brass, pewter, stone, pottery, wooden or basketware containers.

Birthday Party Flowers

Birthday party flowers should, of course, complement the person whose party it is. Flowers must be chosen to suit their preferences and not your own, although they must fit in with the surroundings where the party is to be held. For a young girl's party you could try to emphasise the background by arranging large bunches of Queen Anne's Lace, Marguerites, Pinks, Cornflowers, Candytuft, Sweet Peas, or any other pastel-coloured unsophisticated flowers. Tie them up with large bows of pink or apple-green ribbon. These flowers need to be in large bunches so that they can be seen easily, for they have no exotic qualities, and will not stand out in small bunches.

Another idea for the tea table is to make one large central arrangement with ribbons coming from it to each individual place setting. At the end of the ribbons place tiny baskets of flowers or sweets. The young guests will be delighted to take these home at the end of the party.

On the other hand, a similar event staged for an eighteen-year-old girl would require the use of exotic and more sophisticated flowers placed in elegant containers.

Wedding Anniversary Flowers

Wedding anniversaries call for a celebration and the main ones, such as silver and gold, are often celebrated with a party. It is a thoughtful and pleasant idea to introduce, with floral decorations, some of the symbols which are attached to these anniversaries.

A silver wedding, to celebrate twenty-five years of marriage, can have flower arrangements which introduce silver. This can be done by arranging white flowers in a silver bowl or vase with a silver ribbon or tinsel. If you do not have a silver vase, a grey pottery vase can be substituted, or a vase or tin can be covered with silver spray paint. It is in these silver arrangements that good use can be made of the beautiful foliage of silver-leaved shrubs and plants. *Artemisia arborescens* has silver-white leaves and *Senecio maritima* shows the whitest leaves in the garden, 'Silver Dust' and 'Diamond' being the two best varieties. Lamb's Tongue (*Stachys lanata*) is very popular in cottage gardens and 'Silver Carpet' is especially good where foliage is required, as this variety does not produce flowers. Lavender grows in most gardens and its slender blue flowering spikes fit in well with a silver flower arrangement.

White Roses are a fitting flower to arrange among the silver foliage. 'Iceberg' Floribunda Roses, which are perfect in form and also fragrant, make an ideal choice.

Table decorations can incorporate white or silver candles, and silver doilies can be placed under arrangements or used as place mats.

A golden wedding celebration is very special and here gold-coloured flowers can feature. There are so many in this colour range, including Chrysanthemums, Roses,

Gerberas, Carnations, Dahlias, Gladioli and Day Lilies. These could be arranged in a golden-coloured vase or in a vase or bowl which was an original wedding present. Alternatively, any existing vase or basket can easily be sprayed or painted gold.

It is a charming gesture if the main flower arrangement is designed from the same flowers as the bride carried on her wedding day. The table covering can be gold lamé or gauze, and candles with the number fifty marked on them in gold can be placed in the centre of the table. Celebrate with a cake, bound in a gold frill, and use gold paper doilies. The number fifty should be a prominent feature and this can be cut out of cardboard and covered with gold paper or painted gold. The celebration drink of course should be sparkling wine or champagne.

It is not only the main wedding anniversaries which can be exploited when planning flowers. The symbols can be interpreted however you like and they offer a wide choice to stimulate the flower arranger's imagination, and would probably make an interesting subject for a competition.

1st – Cotton	10th – Tin
2nd – Paper	15th – Crystal
3rd – Leather	20th – China
4th – Fruit and Flowers	25th – Silver
5th – Wooden	30th – Pearl
6th – Sugar	35th – Coral
7th – Woollen	40th – Ruby
8th – Salt	50th – Golden
9th – Copper	60th – Diamond

Some of the most successful parties I have attended or given have been planned around the flowers. I admit that the food and drink are very important, but guests will often remember long after the event that 'burst of yellow and white flowers' or that 'large pedestal group of red flowers spot-lit from above'.

The colour of the main arrangements can be re-echoed at other strategic points, in a hall or on the dining table, or even placed in small tins or jars up the stairs (providing the stairs are wide enough), to add to the general impact of colour which is so important.

Cocktail Party Arrangements

Flowers should play an important part as decorations at a cocktail party, and if their use is exaggerated they can assume a star role. If the party is held in the early part of the year, try using only Mimosa and Daffodils in the arrangements. The flowers must be used profusely, displaying masses of them on mantelshelves, tables and pedestals so that they become the talk of the party and are remembered long after they have died.

A May Day cocktail party could have the theme of blossom branches and Lily of the Valley. The small white flowers of this delicate flower hang down in tiny round bells from pale green stems and will be most effective if they are placed in water-filled glass tubes, and then inserted into a cone or tree of greenery. Try spraying

some Lily of the Valley cologne around or, if the party is at night, place some Lily of the Valley perfume on the electric light bulbs. The heat will release the scent; but do use it sparingly as there is nothing worse than over-scented air. During the month of May, when Tulips abound and Lilac comes into bloom, there is nothing more beautiful than arrangements of these flowers massed around the house. Lilac with its sweet-smelling branches of mauve, purple and white blossom can be used with no other floral additions. But remember to remove all the leaves and allow the split stem ends to stand in deep water overnight. Lilac can be cut short and arranged at the top of a tall candelabra or placed in a low bowl to great effect, especially if the pink, mauve and purple colour scheme is emphasised with pink table cloths and pink tinted drinks are served. Gin and champagne can be turned pink by adding a few drops of Angostura bitters. If the party is in the evening, try fixing a spot-light to focus on the Lilac, as this overcomes the problem of purple and mauve flowers appearing dull. Pinks show up especially well when artificial light is shone on them.

The ideas for specialised flower arrangements are endless. I once used a red theme, using flowers of all tints and shades of this exciting colour. The arrangements were placed around the house and on the serving table. The only relief was given by a frill of apple-green ribbon placed around a posy of Carnations which I set on the curled banister at the foot of the stairs. This was held firmly in place with adhesive tape. Flowers of one colour are sure to be noticed and are certain to create a greater impact than if vases of various coloured blooms are dotted about the house.

For a cocktail party held in mid-summer, all-white or white and green flowers will create a cool effect. Daisies, Roses, Hellebores and any of the other beautiful summer flowers can be used. The colour scheme can be heightened by bowls of green apples, dishes of green olives, cheese-filled celery on a bed of lettuce and the addition of green candles. The tablecloth can be criss-crossed with green ribbon, the ends of which can be weighted down with bunches of greenery pinned to the cloth.

One point to remember is that arrangements for cocktail parties must be placed high up as the guests will be standing most of the time and low arrangements will be obscured from view.

Buffet Party Arrangements

Buffet parties are perhaps the most delightful way of entertaining friends and guests. There is a casualness about them which allows the hostess after all her hard work to relax and enjoy the company of her guests. The guests will either be served or help themselves to food from a large table.

The flower arrangements for a buffet table are best if a candelabra or tall-stemmed container is used. This allows the arrangement to be seen from across the room as well as leaving more space on the table for dishes. The arrangement can be placed either in the centre of the table with the drinks at one end and the food at the other, or a tall decoration can be placed at each end of the serving table with the food placed centrally.

If it is possible to place the buffet table in front of the fireplace, the mantelshelf and the surrounds can be decorated with flowers and trailing foliage. The decorations, whether of fruit and flowers or flowers and foliage or just bright tablecloths with candles placed in wine bottles, will all help to add to the general relaxed atmosphere.

If your setting will allow it, try to include vines or trailing creepers in your decorative scheme and combine these with bunches of grapes together with ears of wheat and barley and bright informal flowers.

For a home setting which is formal, there can be nothing more lovely than grapes and vines with a few flowers spilling over from the rims of fine china vases or compote dishes. Candlelight, whether from candles in a candelabra or wine bottles, is ideally suited to the mellow atmosphere of a wine and cheese party.

Many variations are possible for a special buffet party, and different themes can be interpreted with the use of suitable containers and floral material. For instance, if the party food includes a special fish dish, the theme can be emphasised with shell containers, making use of all the different shapes and colours of shells which are available. Fishing nets can be included in the main arrangements or draped and placed around the base of the buffet table.

Formal Dinner Party Flowers

The flower arrangements for a dinner party will be affected by several different things. The colour of the china and tablecloth, as well as the size and shape of the table will all have to be taken into account.

For a large oblong table, flowers are usually placed low in the centre and flanked each side with tall candlestick arrangements. Tall designs are fine as long as they do not interfere with guests, who must be able to converse easily across the table. There is nothing more annoying than a flower arrangement which continually gets in the way.

To make a candlestick arrangement, insert a candle cup holder into the top of the candlestick, holding it firm with plasticine or adhesive clay. Fill it with floral foam and insert a candle, pressing it down right through the foam, or better still use a candle holder. The flowers can then be inserted around the base of the candle with stems of Ivy or similar material swerving downwards. A candelabra can be decorated in the same way, but this will very much depend on the shape and style of the candelabra. Some will have only two candle sockets and these can have the flowers placed in the centre above the supporting column. Ivy or other trailing greenery can be used to stretch down and along the centre of the table to join up with the low central design.

Ideally, the container for a low central design should match the candlesticks, but this is not absolutely necessary as not a lot of it will be seen, so almost any bowl or vegetable tureen, filled with floral foam, can be used.

Make the low centrepiece about 25 cm (10 inches) or 30 cm (12 inches) high and as wide as the table will allow. A general guide is to make the arrangement one-sixth of the table length. Insert the chosen flowers in a horizontal design, using fairly choice flowers for a special dinner party. The design must be equally viewable from all sides,

OPPOSITE: *The grouping of fruit on the green fabric-covered base provides the finishing touch for this striking buffet party arrangement.*
BELOW: *The pink cloth gives emphasis to the pale pink flowers in this well-proportioned table arrangement.*

and try not to use flowers which have a heavy scent as this will interfere with the aroma of the food and wines.

Fruit is an attractive addition to a flower centrepiece, but make sure you add the fruit while you are arranging the flowers, finally allowing some of the flowers to protrude from among the fruit. If the fruit is added at the end it will look as though it has been included as an after-thought and will not form an integrated part of the design.

Candles should be of a matching or contrasting colour. If they are placed in the refrigerator until they are ready to be used they will burn down more slowly.

Round tables will look best with a solid round arrangement in the centre of the table. Unless you have a special reason for using certain colours, try to use flowers of a colour which will echo the china being used, the tablecloth or even a dominant note in the room. If the table is large enough, four candlesticks can be placed equally around the arrangement.

It is not only tables that require arrangements at a dinner party; if you have a sideboard or serving table this will take an arrangement. Many people have paintings or prints on their dining-room walls. If these are of flowers, a charming idea is to copy the flower arrangement which is depicted in the painting. If possible try to pick or buy identical flowers; otherwise, substitute similar flowers of the same colour. It is always interesting to see how many guests notice the reproduction flower arrangement.

CANDLES AND FLOWERS

Candles are made in every conceivable size, shape and colour, from small squat straight-sided ones to tall barley-sugar twists. Few combinations associate as well as flowers and candles. Tall candles give height to a low grouping of flowers; they add colour contrast or harmony to any decoration, whether they are lit or not. Grouped together in various colours, they can form an exciting decoration with a few flowers added.

In a rustic setting, try placing candles in colourings of cream, tan and brown into a block of wet floral foam. Add a few flame-red Chrysanthemums at the base to conceal the foam. The candles give height and only a few flowers are needed.

The glow which lighted candles produce adds a touch of intimacy which other lighting seems to disperse, and for this reason in winter-time, when flowers are expensive and scarce, a few candles are welcome for any type of table decoration.

A selection of candles in pale pink, deep pink, crimson and cerise are most effective when grouped with pink Chrysanthemums and Anemones on a table. For a party effect, you might like to combine brilliant turquoise blue chunky-shaped candles with silver painted leaves. One of the easiest table decorations can be made by standing a chunky green candle on a block of wet floral foam which has been placed on a cake stand. Insert short-stemmed flower-heads, such as yellow single Chrysanthemums, into the foam to make the candle appear as if it is standing in a ring of flowers. This type of arrangement needs only two stems of spray Chrysanthemums, which is a great saving at the times of the year when flowers are very expensive.

If you are especially fond of pressed flowers, these can be used to decorate the sides of candles. The flowers can either be glued onto the candle or held in place with a pin pushed through the centre of the flowers and then into the side of the candle. Once the flat flower petals are in place they can be covered with varnish or melted candle wax. Pink flowers on purple candles or vice versa are a most attractive colour combination. These flower-covered candles make delightful and very personal presents.

Candles placed in the neck of a wine bottle can be made more decorative if they are encircled with flowers or foliage. Place a thick ring of plasticine around the neck of the bottle and insert sprigs of greenery and berries into the clay. Artificial flowers can also be used, mixed in with natural greenery.

If the candles are too big for the top of the wine bottle or candlestick they are to be placed in, dip the ends in hot water for a minute or two and then press them into place. In the absence of a candle holder, bind four cocktail sticks or hair-pins to the base of the candle with adhesive tape. These prongs can then be inserted into the floral foam to hold the candle firmly upright.

When extinguishing candles, you can avoid spilling the hot wax if you place your forefinger close to your lips, horizontally, and blow across it.

Flowers Through the Seasons

As the seasons change so does the choice and availability of flowers. In the cold winter months the flower arranger has to rely greatly on flowers from the florist, winter-flowering shrubs and evergreen foliage. This is a far cry from the abundance of flowers which fill the shops and gardens during the spring and summer months. But whatever the time of year, the dedicated flower arranger will always find some form of floral material to use.

SPRING

When daisies pied and violets blue
And lady-smock all silver-white
And cuckoo-buds of yellow hue
Do paint the meadows with delight,
WILLIAM SHAKESPEARE

After the sparse choice of flowers in winter the advent of spring flowers is a delight. The small delicate flowers which grow close to the ground so as to be sheltered from the wind, such as Primroses, Violets and Snowdrops, can be arranged in dainty glass containers or china bowls. The slightly longer-stemmed Grape Hyacinths, Scillas and Dwarf Narcissi arranged in a blue and white china tea cup and saucer and placed on a coffee or small side table make a fresh looking arrangement.

Yellow is a very predominant colour among spring flowers, the most common being the Daffodils and Narcissi. These should be bought or picked when they are in bud as they open very quickly once they are placed in a warm environment; but do not pick the buds until some yellow is showing as totally green buds will not open once they are picked. There are many different varieties of Daffodils and Narcissi, varying in size as well as colour. Try and include some of the blooms which have a different coloured centre cup to the outer petals in your arrangements. Narcissus 'Armada' with an orange cup and yellow petals, 'Tudor Minstrel' with a yellow frill-edged cup and overlapping white petals, and the 'Actaea' Narcissus with white petals and small yellow cup edged with dark crimson are just some of the many to choose from. These long-stemmed flowers look beautiful when arranged in a formal arrangement which includes blue Irises and bronze Tulips.

An all-yellow arrangement can look just as fine using all-yellow Daffodils, yellow Irises, yellow Tulips and long thin delicate sprays of Jasmine or Forsythia and Pussy Willow.

A delightful way to combine the short- and long-stemmed spring flowers is to make a small garden arrangement on a large dinner or meat plate. Place a pin-holder in a shallow dish of water at the back of the plate and arrange tall sprays of Pussy Willow and Catkins at the back of the holder. Daffodils of various lengths can be placed in the centre. These should look as if they are all coming from one central point. Cover the plate with moss and if you can find different varieties of moss, this will add extra interest and texture to the design. Insert small water-filled tubes or aspirin bottles under the moss at the front and sides of the plate. Place bunches of short, delicate-stemmed flowers in these, such as Primroses, Aconites, Violets or any other spring flower you can find.

These will look as if they are growing out of the moss. Pieces of bark or stone can be placed on the moss to add to the natural look of the design. Providing the bottles are kept topped up with water and the moss is kept damp, this small seasonal garden should give pleasure for a long time.

Spring produces some of the most beautiful blossoms and flowering shrubs and these add beauty to any home. You will only need a few branches of heavily laden blossom as too much blossom would detract from the natural beauty of the arched branches. Blossom is best picked when it is in tight bud as it opens rapidly once it is brought inside. The Prunus family offers the greatest variety of ornamental blossom and this includes Cherry, Almond, Plum and Peach, which all flower at different times from February through to May.

One of my favourite spring flowering shrubs is Corylopsis with its racemes of pale yellow flowers which appear in March and April. Three curved sprays of this sweet-smelling shrub are enough when placed in a tall container or bottle. Other flowering shrubs are Azaleas and Philadelphus, often called Mock Orange.

There are so many different spring flowers and shrubs that it is impossible to mention them all but by experimenting with cultivated as well as wild flowers, your arrangements should be a delight to all who see them.

SUMMER

There is an abundance of flowers to choose from in the summer. Tall blue Delphiniums, Larkspur, Canterbury Bells and daisy-shaped flowers, Godetias, Carnations and spikes of Gladioli are just a few, but perhaps the most beautiful summer flowering bloom is the Rose. Probably no other flower has been endowed with as many legends as the Rose. Mythology tells us that its birth coincided with that of Venus, the Goddess of Love. In the language of flowers the Rose is the symbol of love.

Almost everyone loves a Rose and certainly no flower is more beautiful when arranged in the home. Colour and variety is a matter of personal choice, but the choice is so wide there is hardly an occasion when the correct Rose is not available.

If you grow Roses in your garden, you will grow those you prefer. Always remember to cut them before they are fully open: so many people leave the blooms on the bushes until they are almost fully blown, then wonder

The arrangement of spring Tulips with a slanting branch of Ivy and contorted Willow perfectly complements the style of this room.

why they do not last well indoors. Cut your Roses, above a leaf joint whenever possible, then, on reaching the house, remove the lower leaves and scrape off the thorns which will be below the waterline of your container. Split the stem ends with a knife or floral scissors, and stand the stems in deep water for several hours to condition them.

Use non-patterned, simple containers so as not to detract from the beauty of the Roses. There is no doubt that the ideal container for Roses is a bowl of one sort or another, for here they can be arranged in masses, with foliage, so that they look as natural as possible. A pin-holder can be placed in the base of a modern bowl and then filled with crumpled wire-netting to give added support to the stems.

Roses grow in many different varieties. The Floribunda Roses have single, semi-double or double flowers in clusters, and it is best to clip out some of the more open heads to avoid a thick and heavy arrangement. The removed flower-heads can be used in wine glasses or floated on the top of a small glass bowl filled with water.

The Hybrid Tea Rose and the Garnette type of Rose are very good varieties for cutting as they last well in water. White Roses such as 'Virgo' and 'Iceberg' are ideal for weddings, and the pink varieties 'Dearest' and 'Queen Elizabeth' are perfect for home decoration. Yellow and orange coloured Roses are perhaps the best for parties and receptions held in the evening as they show up well. But, for those who wish to be a little different, there are many unusual colours to choose from, such as mauve, silver, brown and bicolours.

Roses recommended for their Colour

Yellow	Orange
Young Quinn	Bettina
Grandpa Dickson	Just Joey
Princess Michael of Kent	Whisky Mac
Sutter's Gold	Doris Tysterman
Gold Crown	Orange Belinda
Red	**Pink**
Fragrant Cloud	Royal Highness (pale)
Alec's Red	Lady Seton (deep)
Deep Secret	Queen Elizabeth
National Trust	Dearest
Ruby Wedding	Bridal Pink
Cream/White	**Unusual colours**
Moon Maiden	Silver Charm (lilac)
Pascali	Tom Brown (two-toned brown)
Margaret Merrill	News (purple red)
Iceberg	Julia's Rose (chocolate/ parchment)
Rose Landia	Grey Dawn (soft grey)

Providing they are conditioned properly cut Roses should last well, but if a Rose wilts at the top, just remove it and re-cut the stem and stand it in 5 cm (2 inches) of hot water for some hours. This should revive it and it can then be replaced in the arrangement. There are a number of commercial products on the market devised for helping flowers to last longer. If you do not have one of these products to hand, a teaspoon of sugar to a pint of water will help.

AUTUMN

Early autumn sees an end to the abundance of bright coloured summer flowers and the garden and countryside take on a golden appearance. The leaves begin to turn to the beautiful tawny reds and yellows of October as the cold weather halts the flow of sap to the leaves. Flowers are not plentiful, but there are still a few Dahlias and Crinums to be found and of course the ever-faithful Chrysanthemum to add extra colour to an arrangement of autumn foliage.

The bronze, yellow and deep pink colours of Chrysanthemums harmonise well with the tinted foliage, and by using different shaped flowers an exciting and varied decoration can be made. The light bronze thread-petalled 'Bronze Rayonnate' and the anemone-centred 'Catena' are both a joy to behold. The bronze, single-flowering 'Mason's Bronze' with its daisy-like yellow centres is ideal for arranging with bright yellow and flame-coloured berries. The yellow spray type, such as 'Yellow Marble', the spider type, like 'Golden Crystal', will look especially fine if arranged with some dark shiny green-yellow leaves, such as *Elaeagnus pungens* 'Maculata', Rhododendron, or Golden Privet (*Ligustrum*).

A charming autumnal arrangement can be made using only foliage, making full use of the russet-coloured foliage available from the garden and countryside. The small leaves of Tellima, an evergreen perennial, turn a beautiful copper bronze colour in autumn, and *Sorbus sargentiana* turns bright red. *Fothergilla monticola*, with orange, red and yellow tinted leaves, and the autumn foliage of *Viburnum dentatum* can also be used to great effect.

Seed-heads can be incorporated among the foliage. There are several different varieties of plants which produce bright red and orange seeds in the autumn. The seed-pods of *Iris foetidissima* split open and curve outwards to reveal scarlet-coloured seeds. The paper-like lantern shaped seed-heads of the Chinese Lantern (*Physalis alkekengi*) add a bright splash of orange to any arrangement. For a darker orange-red, use the variety of Chinese

Lantern called 'Franchetii'. The twining branches of *Celastrus orbiculatus* not only have beautiful autumn leaves but when the leaves fall, clusters of bright scarlet fruit are left behind. These branches can be arranged on their own into an elegant arrangement.

Another idea is to combine fruit with tinted leaves. Fruit can add colour as well as form to a foliage arrangement. For a centre table decoration, a bowl of green apples into which stems of glossy *Choisya ternata* (Mexican Orange) or *Viburnum tinus* are tucked makes an original table decoration. The apples can rest on a block of water-soaked foam which has been wrapped in plastic or cling film as fruit should never be allowed to lie directly on wet foam. The stems of the leaves are inserted into the foam between the apples. There need be little waste attached to such arrangements as the fruit can be eaten once you tire of the design.

In my opinion, there is nothing more lovely in late summer or early autumn than a grouping of pale green grapes and some peaches with autumn-coloured foliage. Some fruits are shiny, some have dull surfaces, so when grouping fruits with leaves try to place dull fruits against shiny leaves and shiny fruits against dull leaves. The two different textures will complement each other, showing each to its advantage.

If you are making a foliage and fruit arrangement in a shallow tray or on a base, place the fruits, such as apples or pears, which are to rest on the base on rubber jar rings or on a thin roll of plasticine. This prevents the fruit from rolling around. Similar round fruit which is to be placed high up in the arrangement can be held in place by fixing it onto a sharp stick. Grapes arranged on foam or wire-netting can be held in place with a hairpin or thick wire.

WINTER

Winter is the time of year when flowers are at their most expensive and it is here that flowering shrubs and evergreen foliage can be used to their best advantage. An arrangement of leaves can have a few flowers added for extra colour; although if you study the many forms, shapes, sizes and colours of leaves, you can create the most interesting decorations using only foliage. Follow the same principles of design as for other arrangements, using the taller pointed leaves for the outline and placing the larger rosette type in the centre. Fill in with less important leaves. If you are making a modern design from leaves, place the tall pointed leaves on a pin-holder, to give height, and insert some broader and shorter ones lower down as transition. Add a few larger, rounder, more dominant leaves at the base of the arrangement for focal interest.

The great variety of colour in the world of leaves helps to make an arrangement more effective. Some shrubs have bright coloured berries throughout the winter and some even bear flowers. These can be arranged with leaves or on their own. The Berberis family contains many berried varieties, the scarlet berries of *Berberis thunbergii* and the coral-red fruits of *Berberis × rubrostilla* borne on arching branches are just two examples of many. *Cotoneaster* 'Cornubia', a semi-evergreen shrub, has branches which are heavily laden with red fruits.

The Snowberry (*Symphoricarpos*) bears white berries on its arched branches from October onwards. Perhaps the finest winter flowering shrub is Mahonia. This dark green shiny-leaved shrub has bright yellow clusters of flowers during the winter months. *Mahonia* 'Charity' has long spikes of sweet-smelling deep yellow flowers, and *Mahonia bealii* has lemon-yellow flowers.

Winter-flowering Jasmine can be arranged with variegated leaves to make a light and delicate arrangement, and sprays of Golden Privet (*Ligustrum*) can form the background for yellow Chrysanthemums, creating a bright arrangement during the long winter months.

Whatever plant material you are using, remember that it must be conditioned before being arranged. Most leaves, except the grey ones which lose their delicate colouring if submerged in water, should be soaked in water for some hours in order to completely fill their water channels. They will last longer if you add a little sugar to the water; this helps by forming a faint film over the underside pores, which prevents loss of moisture through transpiration.

When cutting from evergreen shrubs, remember that it is better to cut from the back and underneath as this is usually where the interesting curves are to be found. Or you can cut from the centre of the shrub which will thin it out, but always cut just above an outward pointing bud.

All woody shrubs should have the stem ends split and some of the lower bark removed before submerging them in water. Floral foam can be used to support the leaves in the container but it is better to place the leaves in clear water, using wire-netting to hold the stems in place.

Here is a list of some of my favourite evergreen leaves which I would not be without:

Mahonia aquifolium	Skimmia
Viburnum tinus	Camellia
Choisya ternata	Ribes
Elaeagnus pungens 'Maculata'	Euonymus
Ligustrum (Privet)	Rhododendron
Aucuba japonica (Spotted Laurel)	*Escallonia radicans* 'Silver Queen'
Fatsia japonica	*Lonicera nitida*

In addition, one must not forget the different Ivies, and when any foliage is difficult to find house plants can be grouped together. Vigorously growing house plants will not suffer if some of their leaves are removed. You can always cut from the green climber *Cissus antarctica*, commonly known as the Kangeroo Vine, and *Tradescantia fluminensis* 'Quicksilver' will constantly give variegated trails. If a burst of strap-like leaves are required for central interest, then try to grow Chlorophytum (Spider Plant) which benefits from regular pruning.

Christmas Decorations

At Christmas time the world glows with loving thoughts. Smiles are exchanged, quarrels forgotten, presents given, kind messages written and a general atmosphere of goodwill descends everywhere. It is in the home that this atmosphere is more pronounced than elsewhere, for it is here that family parties mainly take place: dinners, suppers, cocktail parties, and buffet lunches.

The Christmas tree is usually the focal point of all the decorations and the fresh green and red theme can be carried out all through the house. This includes the use of evergreens, red ribbons and coloured glass baubles. However, there are all kinds of different colour schemes, such as pink and silver, red and gold, turquoise, purple, copper and, of course, white. Once you have chosen your colour scheme, it is a good idea to repeat it all through the home.

If the Christmas tree is to be displayed in the vicinity of an open fire, it will be less of a fire hazard if you fireproof it. Mix 60 grammes (2 oz) of ammonia phosphate, obtained from a chemist, with just under 4.5 litres (1 gallon) of water, and after standing the tree outside on a piece of newspaper, spray or splash it with this solution.

Trees which are fresh will not burn easily, so it is not so necessary to fireproof them. It should however stand in a tub of wet soil, or wet crumpled newspaper. If it has roots, re-cut the dry root ends and add a teaspoonful of fertiliser to the water or soil to help stimulate fresh green growth. You can also spray the tree with S.100 to preserve moisture and prevent needle drop.

If you enjoy a gold and glitter effect you can lightly spray the tree with gold paint, adding red bows on the branches. Echo this idea with a table centrepiece made with gilded leaves, fruit and red candles. A hanging decoration can be made by tying a cluster of golden baubles with red ribbon and hanging them from a light pendant.

It is wise to plan the scheme and the number of arrangements you will need well in advance, then set aside an afternoon for the painting and glittering. Fir cones and other short items will need false stems of wire, and longer

A mass of greenery provides the background for this large pedestal group, which includes Gladioli, Gerberas, Auratum Lilies, Rowan berries and Croton.

sprays of leaves, such as Beech and Eucalyptus, should be preserved in glycerine and water first, otherwise the leaves will shrivel. Do this, as well as gathering Teazels and seed-heads, during August and September, keeping them in a box or cupboard until required. Leaves can be preserved by standing the stem ends for three weeks in a solution of one part glycerine to two parts hot water.

There are a number of gold and silver aerosol spray paints, which will quickly cover leaves, gourds, cones and other suitable materials. A cheaper method is to put the paint on with a brush. Many jewel-like metallic spray paints can be obtained from car paint suppliers or in powder form from art supply shops. Whichever method you choose, be sure to cover the working surface and surrounds with plenty of newspaper, to prevent any paint from getting on the furniture or floor. Before the painted surface is dry, glitter can be sprinkled on, but if you have large areas to cover it is best to put the glitter into a sugar sifter rather than shaking it straight from the tube. The edges of flowers, leaves, seed-pods and grasses can be brushed lightly with glue and then dipped into glitter. Guests' names can be written in glue on place settings or on the sides of glass baubles and then sprinkled with glitter. A small bottle of white spirit is a handy asset at this time, for mistakes are sure to be made.

The centrepiece for the Christmas table can become a talking point among friends and family. The design should be considered carefully, taking into account the colour of the cloth, the flowers and the accessories, as well as the china and glass. Whether it takes the form of a 'scene' or extends the colour theme you intend featuring

in other parts of the house, something different is always appreciated by guests. You could lay a red cloth and place a white snow scene made from plaster of Paris in the centre, repeating the idea for place settings. These tiny place settings can be made by filling a tin lid with wet plaster and inserting some greenery and ornaments into it.

Conversely, you can plan with a white tablecloth in mind, placing a wide red ribbon down the whole length of the table, finishing the design with an arrangement in the centre. This centrepiece could be made from a block of wet floral foam into which red Carnations are inserted with leaves or Holly. If you do not object to them, there is a mass of beautiful artificial flowers available from department stores and florists which can be used instead of fresh flowers.

To make a table centrepiece, start by placing a block of wet floral foam pressed onto a pin-holder for stability, in a shallow dish perhaps set on a tray or a base. Insert a tall candle for height, followed by long leaves of silver, gold or green low down at the sides to give width to the arrangement. Work towards the centre with shorter leaves and flowers, making some of them point forwards and some backwards. Finish in the centre with baubles and flowers, adding fruit (on sticks) if you like. Christmas time offers a great chance to show skill and expression with table decorations.

Door and hanging decorations are very popular, especially the swag of greenery at the front door which spells welcome to all who visit us at Christmas. As an alternative to a block of floral foam into which you can insert greenery, try cutting a potato in half lengthwise and then tie it up like a parcel with red ribbon. Finally insert greenery, pine cones and other suitable floral material into the potato. The cut potato will keep the greenery fresh and a red bow and streamers can be added before the decoration is hung on the door.

For a traditional Christmas wreath to hang on the front door you will require a base. Florists supply special foam or moss covered rings, or you can make one from a metal

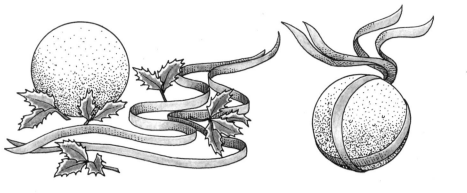
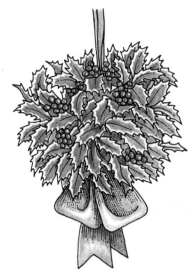

coat hanger. This is done by pulling the coat hanger into a circular shape and then covering it with moss or tape. Secure the moss to the wire with reel wire or string, or bind with tape. This prevents anything else you might bind to the frame from slipping. Short sprigs of greenery can now be bound onto the ring, adding false berries, fir cones and other items as desired. A large wadge of plasticine can be tied on at the top underneath the hook, and here larger sprays, cones and a ribbon bow can be inserted. Bind the coat hanger hook with ribbon and hang up the wreath with another bow.

For a wreath which is to hang inside, more exotic colours and materials can be used. Excellent plastic-covered wire rings, called lamp pendants, can be bought at the haberdashery department in large stores. These rings can be covered with red ribbon and finished with greenery and a collection of leaves, imitation fruit and fir cones which have had the tips of their scales painted white.

White polystyrene ceiling tiles can be cut into different shapes and decorated to form hanging decorations, but few decorations are as attractive as a Holly ball tied up with red ribbon and suspended from a light or the ceiling of a hall. To make this you will need a sphere of floral foam, some thin red ribbon and some green berried Holly. Cut two lengths of ribbon which are long enough to pass around the ball and leave enough to make a loop to hang the decoration up with. Tie these two lengths of ribbon around the ball so that they cross at right angles to one another at the base of the ball, with the loose ends all together at the top. Insert Holly into the ball until it is completely covered. Small red glass balls can be given a wire stem and placed among the Holly if desired.

Another hanging decoration can be made in the same way as a Holly ball but, instead of Holly, insert toothpicks all over the sphere. When the sphere is completely covered spray the whole thing with paint and, when it is dry, brush with glue and sprinkle with glitter. Small Christmas tree decorations can be made in the same way, using glass- or pearl-headed pins instead of toothpicks.

Apples, gourds or pine cones can all be tied into a hanging group for a door or wall. These will appear more exciting if finished at the top with a lavish ribbon bow or greenery such as Yew, Pine or Fir.

Few of us can resist the magical effect of an all-white Christmas, and once you have decided on such a scheme the rest is not difficult with the aid of white matt paint, plaster of Paris, artificial snow, or soap flakes. Large branches of Yew, Fir or bare twigs and large seed-heads can be dipped into a pail of white oil-based distemper and then hung up to dry. If distemper is not available, try filling a bucket with water and then gently pour a layer of an oil-based paint onto the surface. Dip the items through the paint into the water; as you draw them out the paint will hold.

Smaller leaves and cones can be covered with white shoe cleaner or white paint. For a snowy effect to cover large branches or the Christmas tree, try whisking up a large basin of soap flakes with water (it should be thick and fluffy), then flick this mixture all over the surface. It will settle like snow. Alternatively, white paint and artificial snow is available in aerosol sprays at household and department stores.

White, if used alone, can appear cold, so as an effective contrast try adding greenery or bright bows of red or green ribbon to your designs. Silver or coloured glitter can be sprinkled on before the paint dries and glittering glass baubles can be hung from white-painted bare branches.

However many bright decorations we use, fresh white flowers never fail to give pleasure. Combine these with a religious figure or simply arrange them with beautiful foliage to gently remind us of the meaning of Christmas.

Preserving Flowers and Foliage

Gone are the days when an arrangement of dry flowers consisted of some pressed Ferns, Teazels and a few Helichrysums. Today the drying, preserving and arranging of dried flowers has become an art which is practised by many flower arrangers.

I recall very vividly the occasion when my eyes were opened to the possibilities of preserving flowers. It was at the International Flower Show held in New York in 1947 and I had been asked to display an orchid which had been given to one of the guests at Princess Elizabeth's wedding from the top of the wedding cake. The orchid had been flown from England to America packed in a gas mask as boxes were in short supply at that time. Since the wedding had taken place several months before I was hesitant, thinking the flower would be dead, but I was informed that it had been dehydrated at the Botanical Gardens with the aid of Borax powder. This was my first introduction to the preserving of exotic and colourful flowers and I returned to England to experiment myself and later gave a lecture and demonstration on this fascinating subject.

Although some people are lucky enough to have access to growing material all the year round there are many others, who live in towns and cities, who will find that preserved flowers and foliage are a very useful stand-by, as well as making delightful arrangements. Preserved flowers are particularly useful during the winter months when fresh flowers are expensive to buy. In most homes there is nearly always one place where a permanent arrangement of dried flowers can stand. Dried flowers are also useful time-savers, as they can be prepared in advance and brought out only when they are needed.

Botanical Gardens have for many years practised the preserving of certain specimens and some beautiful examples can be seen at Kew Gardens in London. Recently a method of preserving flowers has been investigated by several Museums and Universities which has resulted in delicate flower arrangements being 'freeze dried'. However this is not a method which is used by flower arrangers in general and the four most common methods of drying and preserving are:
(1) the air drying method; (2) the powdered desiccants or burying method; (3) the glycerine and water method; (4) the pressing method.

Each of these methods should be studied as different flowers and foliage require different methods.

The Upside-Down Air Drying Method

This method suits flowers which grow in tall spires. The flowers should be picked before they are fully open and mature. Try to pick them on a fine day when they are not covered with dew. Tie the flowers into small bundles and hang them upside-down in a dark, warm cupboard or room. When they are dried, pack them away until they are required in the autumn or winter. This method leaves the flowers slightly shrivelled, but otherwise dry, and the darkness in which they are dried will prevent the colours of the flowers from fading. Air drying suits most seedheads and sprays such as Acanthus (Bear's Breeches) and

LEFT: *Pink and white Helipterums and Helichrysums are natural everlasting flowers grown from seed. Here they are massed in a basket with other air-dried flowers.*
OPPOSITE: *Air-dried flowers can be tied in small bunches with wire, then inserted into blocks of floral foam or tied to a dome of wire-netting in a large container.*

Dock, as well as summer flowers such as Astilbe, Larkspur, Lythrum, Delphinium, Golden Rod and Echinops (Globe Thistle). Long tassels of 'Love-lies-bleeding' (*Amaranthus caudatus*) should be stood up in a jar so that the tassels dry to the shape which occurs when they are alive. If they are hung upside-down they dry like stiff pokers.

The Burying Method

Many open-faced flowers, such as Zinnias, Marguerites, Scabious and Marigolds all preserve well if buried in silica-gel powder. This can be done in a large wooden or cardboard box. A mixture of half-and-half borax and alum powder can be used instead, although silica-gel is the best to use as it dries the flowers more quickly.

I prefer to use dried, open-faced flowers as focal interest in an arrangement with bare branches or preserved Beech leaves. I do not care for a complete arrangement of dried summer flowers since they seem to look so sad during the grey winter months. When mixing fresh and dried flowers together it is best to varnish the lower stems of the dried flowers or to dip them in hot candle wax to prevent them rotting in the water which is so essential for the fresh flowers. Conversely, I love an arrangement of dried twigs, seed-heads and leaves.

Cover the bottom of a box or biscuit tin with a layer of powdered borax or silica-gel. Since the stems of some dried flowers will break off because they are so brittle, a false stem can be added by inserting a hairpin-shaped piece of wire down through the centre of the flower and twisting the two ends together under the calyx. Lay the flowers on the surface of the powder and pour more powder over and around them, lifting the petals now and then as you pour. This makes sure that the powder goes both under and into the flower-head, helping the bloom to retain its shape. If using borax, leave the flowers in the powder for about three weeks, taking great care when you eventually remove them for they will now be brittle and dry. Three days are sufficient for flowers which have been buried in silica-gel and as this powder remains dry, it can be shaken off and used again.

I have dried a complete corsage in this manner and some Dahlias which I dried three years ago (using silica-gel) still look fresh and bright. Many varieties of open flower can be dried this way and it is great fun experimenting.

It is not only the petals of many flowers which are beautiful. The Carnation, for instance, has a beautifully shaped, pale green calyx and when the petals have been removed it looks like a small and delicate green tulip. I have also dried the 'saucer' part of *Cobaea scandens* – a pale green climbing flower which can be grown from seed. This flower looks like a Canterbury Bell, and when the bell drops off I fix a false stem to the green 'saucer' and dry it. Dimorphotheca, commonly called Star of the Veldt, also dries well in silica-gel: fascinating adaptations of these blooms can be made by clipping the petals of similar shaped flowers such as Heleniums, Gaillardias, Rudbeckias and the other types of daisy flowers and drying only the centres. The brown centres with small tufts of colour round the edges give interest to dried decorations.

The Glycerine and Water Method

Most leaves carried on woody-stemmed branches are preserved in this way. The glycerine and water method of preservation is an excellent way of ensuring a good supply of foliage for the background of arrangements throughout the winter.

Wash all leaves and remove any damaged or unwanted foliage. Split the stems of the branches, scraping off some of the bark, and stand them at least 8 cm (3 inches) deep in a solution of two parts hot water and one part glycerine. Leave them there for two or three weeks until the solution has been absorbed. Naturally the leaves will turn brown. A mottled effect can be achieved by removing some of the leaves when they are only half preserved or standing branches in the solution at different times of the year. Beech leaves can be preserved in June through to September to give different shades of brown. Do not leave any branches in the water and glycerine solution for too long or the branches will sweat and attract mildew.

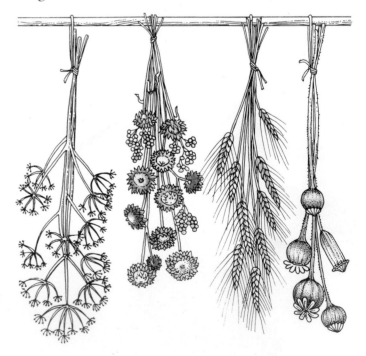

Fleshy-stemmed leaves will not absorb this solution, but branches of *Magnolia grandiflora*, Laurel, Pittosporum, Beech, Laurustinus and Mahonia will take it up quite well and remain preserved indefinitely.

I have fully submerged large, soft Fatsia and some smaller leaves such as Ivy and Lily of the Valley.

The Pressing Method

Ferns and other flat-surfaced leaves such as Acer and Plane are preserved by pressing between sheets of newspaper. When dried in this manner the leaves will remain flat but very interesting lines and shapes can be retained. Hosta leaves can be folded double and pressed between sheets of newspaper, as can Iris, Gladioli, Ivy and Raspberry leaves and all Ferns. Some leaves lose their colour when dried slowly (such as the Virginia Creeper) and in this case add a false wire stem first and press the leaves between newspaper with a warm iron. This extracts the moisture more speedily.

Pussy Willow and Bulrushes dry well if they are picked before they mature and are kept out of water. Bulrushes have a tendency to burst open and scatter their fluffy seeds everywhere but this can be avoided if they are sprayed carefully with heavy hair lacquer or thin varnish.

Interesting shapes can be obtained with Broom if it is wrapped in newspaper and bent to the desired shape. Leave it to dry in this position.

Pressed flowers can be used in flower arrangements and also swags. Some people glue them onto fabric or coloured paper to make hanging pictures.

LEFT: *Upside-down air drying method*
ABOVE: *The burying method*

Skeletonising

'Phantom bouquets' made from skeletonised leaves were very much in vogue in Victorian times and these delicate leaves can be used in modern dried flower arrangements to great effect. *Magnolia grandiflora* leaves respond well to this treatment as do Galax, faded Iris and Montbretia leaves. The leaves must be boiled for 30 minutes in 2.5 litres (1 quart) of water to which a dessertspoon of soda has been added. Leave the leaves to cool in the water and then remove them and place them gently on a sheet of paper. Scrape off all the fleshy parts of the leaf from the veins using the back of a knife, taking great care not to split or tear the leaf. Place the remaining skeleton in some water to which bleach has been added and leave it to soak for one hour. Finally rinse under cold water and then wipe the skeletonised leaf with a soft cloth. Place the dry leaf between two sheets of blotting paper or newspaper weighted down with books. Leave it to press overnight.

False stems can be wired onto the skeletonised leaves which can then be arranged with other dried material, adding a light, airy and ethereal appearance to any dried arrangement. This method can be used for Chinese Lanterns (*Physalis alkekengi*) but they should not be pressed.

Skeletonised leaves can be purchased from florists' shops if you do not have time to prepare them yourself.

Other Preserved Plant Material

Half the fun of drying flowers lies in experimenting with the different methods, but not all dried material needs to be processed. Dried acorns can be strung together to look like a bunch of brown grapes, and walnuts can be pierced with a red hot needle and handled in the same way. Ivy roots can be stripped of their bark and then bleached and polished. Pine cones can be cut in half to assume the appearance of rosettes.

Another item which attracts the keen flower arranger during autumn and winter is the dried Hydrangea. These blooms should be left growing until they are fading or past their best and feel like tissue paper to the touch. The colour begins to turn, and if they are cut at this stage and the stems placed in approximately 2.5 cm (1 inch) of water in a warm room, they will slowly dry out as they become deprived of nourishment. (Add a few spots of green ink to the water if you wish to retain a greeny colour.) Not all Hydrangeas dry out alike, so it is as well to attempt to dry a fair number of blooms which will give you a good variety of colour. These blooms also dry well using the upside-down air drying method.

Ikebana

What more can I write about *ikebana* that has not already been written, except to answer the sceptics who think it is not suitable for Western homes. Of course it is. Admittedly, in the West, flowers have had to compete in the past with elaborate backgrounds, beautiful furniture, paintings, sculptures, ornaments, and other treasures and, in consequence, sumptuous bouquets have been required. A sparse linear pattern would have been lost in such settings; but today, omitting the grand houses, the simple restrained style as practised by the Japanese is becoming more and more popular.

One more answer to the critics is that in the West we are inclined to look at our flower arrangements as the results of the growers' skill. In other words, we are horticulturally minded, and as we appraise a flower arrangement we are conscious of the colour and variety of the plant material used, even of the soil in which it was grown and how this is all combined in a design. On the other hand, a Japanese woman would be inspired by a mental picture, or a scene, and would interpret this in a three-dimensional way. She may only need a branch to represent a tree in the distance, some small pieces of greenery for bushes in the foreground, a rock and one or two flowers. All would be carefully considered, and would express her thoughts, her mood, or her dreams. For this reason Japanese flower arrangements are not judged at shows. For how is the judge to know what is in the mind of the arranger?

The word *ikebana* is generally accepted as meaning 'flower arrangement', although other meanings convey 'the placement of living plant material in water'. In Japan there are about 3,000 schools teaching *ikebana*, the principal ones being Sogetsu, Ohara, Ikenobo, Chico, Ichiyo and Saga. Most teach the essentials of simplicity, harmony, love of Nature, asymmetry (symmetry is too static), philosophy and symbolism. One is taught to give oneself up to the creation of a scene, not to an arrangement (which can be transported as merchandise) but to a communion with nature; in fact, the flower arrangement created is less important than the creative act itself.

So how does all this fit in with our modern world? Even the Japanese have to follow the basic styles to familiarise themselves with the feel of the branches and flowers and the technique of getting them into the vase. All this must be learned before they can move on to creative expression, and so it is with us. If we can under-

stand the basic lines and practise them continuously, we will readily appreciate how adaptable *ikebana* is to our present-day homes. Remember also that it is inexpensive in practice as so few flowers are needed.

In most schools two main styles are practised:

Moribana a style mainly used with a pin-holder (needlepoint) in a shallow container.

Nageire a style in which the flowers are placed in an upright container with a *kubari* (crossbar) used to hold the flowers in place.

Both styles practise the outline of three branches or lines to represent Heaven, Man and Earth, and there are many variations of these styles, such as slanting, upright, horizontal, cascade etc. In addition to the two main styles, further studies can be taken in the classical styles, moon vases, modern free style, *avant garde* and abstract. Yet with all this, it is the 'seeing eye', the training of the branches, the feel of the flowers and the careful thought that brings one in touch with nature and possible enlightenment. The finished arrangement is not merely a pretty decoration to the Japanese.

OPPOSITE: *The three main lines of the* Nageire *style.*
BELOW: *The* Moribana *style in a shallow dish.*

The Moribana Style

Without going deeply into the symbolism, let us look at the technique. Basically, three branches are needed for the low *moribana* style plus a few flowers. The pin-holder can be placed to the right or left of the dish, or to the front or back. For the upright style, the first branch or stem should be cut to a length of about twice the width of the container. If the branch is thick it should be cut slantwise and pressed onto the pin-holder with the cut uppermost. Lean it slightly to the right. The second branch is cut to about two-thirds the length of the first branch and is angled pointing forwards towards the right shoulder. The third branch measures about one-third of the tallest branch and is inserted low on the holder at a forward angle pointing towards the left shoulder. (If wished, these directions can be reversed to left or right.) Branches should point forward and upwards and reach towards you, who can be considered as the sun. Having placed your three main

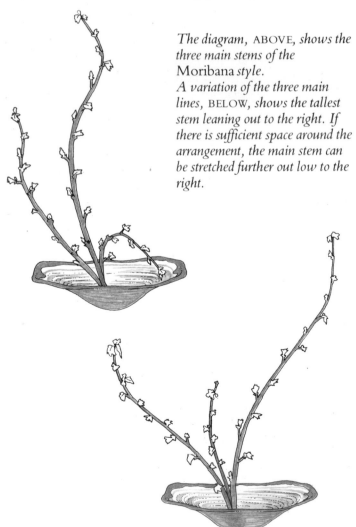

The diagram, ABOVE, shows the three main stems of the Moribana *style.*
A variation of the three main lines, BELOW, shows the tallest stem leaning out to the right. If there is sufficient space around the arrangement, the main stem can be stretched further out low to the right.

stems (Heaven, Man and Earth) you now add the *jushis* or 'fillers' in the vacant area, which can be termed the 'heart' or the 'pool of thought'. There is no restriction as to how many flowers you place here as long as they are of different lengths and not as tall as the main branches. The holder can be covered with leaves or stones or wood.

Variations could be made of this style using similar branches and it is the constant practice of these basic styles and their variations which will denote the ability of the arranger to move upwards and onwards to other styles. All the time it is hoped you will be picking up some of the philosophy of this Japanese art, for only when one is free of thinking about where to place the branches and at what angles, can the mind be emptied for inspiration to arise.

The Nageire Style

The *nageire* style, similar to the *moribana* style, is composed of three main stems which symbolically represent Heaven, Man and Earth. Taking the symbolism a step further, these lines also represent Spiritual Truth, Harmony and Material Substance, which in turn represent the whole of the Universe. All *nageire* arrangements are made in a tall container.

How these three lines are placed in the container is a matter of choice, for there are a number of variations in each style. For instance, you can make a *nageire* in an upright style, slanting style, cascading style or horizontal style, as I have mentioned, but each one would be referred to as 'in the *nageire* style' if it were made in an upright container; the same lines are used, also the variations, just as if they had been made in a low, shallow container. All the variations are given to students as a form of practice, for much practice is required in order to obtain the feel of the branches, their positioning in the container, and the delicate trimming of untidy branches in order to obtain the necessary curved lines.

Many Westerners think it is very difficult to learn all these variations, yet really it is no different from learning how to make a mantelshelf arrangement, or a table arrangement, or a hall arrangement, or an upright vertical arrangement, as we in the West have to learn when placing flowers in the home.

Many find the tall *nageire* style more difficult to achieve than the low *moribana*. This is because in the latter a large pin-holder can be used and this allows you more space, whereas in the *nageire* style there is less space in which to manoeuvre your branches. Traditionally, a *kubari* (crossbar or forked branches) should be used to hold the flowers in place for the *nageire* style.

A cross stick or crossbar fixture is made by cutting two

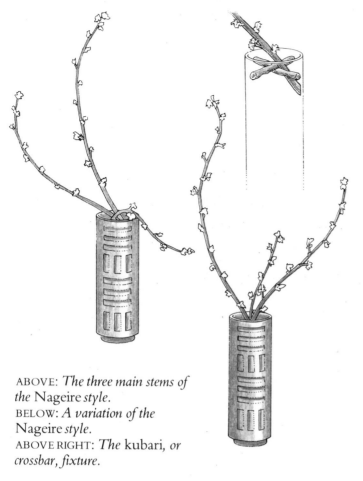

ABOVE: *The three main stems of* the Nageire *style.*
BELOW: *A variation of the* Nageire *style.*
ABOVE RIGHT: *The* kubari, *or crossbar, fixture.*

strong twigs to a size which will enable them, when wired together in the centre, to be wedged firmly in the neck of a cylindrical shaped upright container about 2.5 cm (1 inch) below the rim. You should then insert all the material you are going to use into one of the spaces of the crossbar, which should give the appearance of all the stems rising from the main source. Many modern arrangers are discarding the *kubari* and are using a pin-holder in an upright container which has been three-quarters filled with gravel or sand, giving a false platform on which the holder can stand. The holder can then be placed in a tin of water on top of the gravel, or a false platform can be made by pouring melted wax over the top of the gravel (this prevents the water running down to the bottom).

The basic upright style of *nageire* is composed of the first branch stem, measuring nearly twice the height of the container, being inserted slightly to the left of centre. The second stem, measuring roughly two-thirds that of the first, is placed still leaning slightly to the left but pointing forward. The last stem, measuring one-third that of the first, is inserted low, slanting out to the right and again pointing forward. You do not always have to slant to the left with the first two stems; they can slant to the right if you like but, in this case, the third stem would be placed low out at the left. The flowers are then placed at different angles in the space or the heart of the arrangement, and these should also be of different lengths and placed at various levels, some forward and some right 'in' to create a third dimension.

In the *nageire* slanting style variation, the longest first stem would slant well out to the right, the second stem in the same direction but more upright, and the third stem low and forward to the left.

The Pleasures of Ikebana

What I have described may sound very basic and prosaic; but it is rather like learning our scales at the piano, it has to be done. It is only after the basics become automatic that one is left free to allow the spirit to rise to all the possibilities there are, whether in music or in other modes of artistic expression, such as arranging flowers in the Oriental manner.

Beauty to the Japanese is only apparent in irregularity; therefore, the curves, the asymmetrical outline and the three-dimensional effect are very important. They are conditioned to jagged coastlines, rocky terrain, precipices and mountains, and these effects are portrayed in their flower arrangements. As I have mentioned, they have a scene in mind, rather than horticultural material. In contrast, we in the West look at the plant material which is used in a flower arrangement. We are interested in what it is and how it grows. We, on the whole, grow what we use, while in Japan the flowers are bought. Most Japanese florists offer one bloom and three stems of shrubs beautifully tied up with a bow of coloured string; or you can choose one, two or three items in whatever state you wish, in order to portray your interpretation of the scene you can 'see' in your imagination. If not a scene, it could be a sentiment, a mood or a poem, but it is always in the mind.

Although flower arranging is ephemeral, it is a vital force in the lives of the Japanese people. It is bound up with religion, philosophy and a way of life. I do not presume that this is always true of a new generation brought up in the harsh materialism of the present day, but the subject is still taught in most factories, department stores and offices.

So by practising these basic styles anyone in the West can get the feel of *ikebana* – a style of flower arrangement which is best seen against a plain background. Space is all-important and it is the seeming simplicity of this style which makes it so appealing for modern settings. It also produces a sense of contemplation so welcome in these hurried days.

CHURCH FLOWERS and RECEPTIONS

Flowers play an important part in our lives at home, but it is in church that they take on a special significance. There are many things to consider when arranging flowers in church. The style and architecture must be studied and the arrangements planned to suit the setting. The flowers must also be long lasting, and an understanding of flowers and how they should be prepared and conditioned is essential. An increasing number of people are involved in arranging church flowers and the quiet atmosphere makes the fulfilment of this duty a particular pleasure.

Whether you are planning flowers for a family wedding or a church festival, if you study the significance of the occasion and interpret the idea with flowers, you will ensure that the church message is brought to life.

Church Flowers – a Beginner's Guide

Flowers first appeared in Western churches in the fourth century, when they were placed on the graves of Christians and on the tombs of the Martyrs. By the sixth century the walls of churches were being decorated, though mainly with greenery, as many of the flowers we grow today were unknown in Europe until they were brought back by the Crusaders of the twelfth and thirteenth centuries and later by European explorers.

In the thirteenth to fifteenth centuries (a time of intense religious activity), plant symbolism took on great importance, and the Rose, which symbolised the Virgin, was used frequently in churches. Altar flowers were suspended above the altar in a wreath. It is only in the last century that flower arrangements, as we know them today, have appeared on the altar.

Many people will experience and also give great joy by arranging flowers in church. Flower arranging is an expression of skill, knowledge and appreciation, but while you can express yourself however you choose in your own home there are certain rules and regulations which must be taken into account when arranging flowers in church.

The Victorians filled their churches with flowers imitating the ornate and complicated arrangements used in their homes. They occupied every available space in the church with arrangements and potted plants from their conservatories and so completely hid the beautiful lines and details of the building. The trend for simplicity and harmony of modern flower arranging not only adds beauty, but is more sympathetic to the architecture and atmosphere of our churches.

To achieve the best possible effect from your flowers and foliage, the architecture of the church must be carefully considered. Try to follow the style and line of the church. These vary enormously, from the sturdy and robust architecture of the Norman (Romanesque) church with its height and abundance of arches and pillars, to the Gothic church with vertical emphasis (Perpendicular), huge stained-glass windows and delicate tracery.

The Norman interior lends itself to solid and full arrangements, using large quantities of flowers and foliage. Here good use of large-leaved greenery can be made and also branches from shrubs and evergreens. The rounded leaves of the Bergenia, Hosta (Plantain Lily) or Rhubarb can be used, but remember when using very heavy plant material that it must only be arranged in a well-anchored container. Branches of Fatsia, Japonica, Mahonia and Bay Laurel can also be used. Most of these have woody stems which must have the lower few centimetres (inches) split with a knife or secateurs. This allows them to take in more quickly the water they need to keep them alive.

Flowers which are placed in front of stained-glass windows should blend in with the colours of the window. A church with clear windows and slim columns will require delicate and graceful arrangements, while a dark, wooden-panelled church needs light colours, such as white, pale pink or yellow, to bring light into the church. A pale background will not show up pale-hued flowers and an outline of dark foliage, such as Camellia or Beech, would be a good choice as a dark background to throw lighter coloured flowers into prominence.

Preserved foliage is always a useful stand-by as a background, especially where you are limited by the amount of money you can spend on the arrangement (see chapter on Preserving Flowers and Foliage, page 64).

Having studied the design of the church it is also important to study the district in which the church lies, for this will often help you to decide upon the type of flowers to be used. For instance, a very modern church in a newly built community can take flowers with bold, strong lines, such as Gladioli or Arum Lilies incorporated with bare branches; while a more ornately styled church in a settled town will demand richer flowers with more flowing lines. A country church flower arrangement would be quite out of place if sophisticated flowers, such as Carnations or Anthuriums, were used when the surrounding area abounds with wild and cottage garden flowers. The choice, skill and interpretation are yours.

If you are arranging flowers in your local church you will already know the clergyman, but if you are in a strange church you must make yourself known and explain what you wish to do and where you would like the arrangements to stand. Some clergy have fixed ideas about where the flowers should be placed. He will also show you where any rubbish may be put and where the church containers are kept.

Some churches have a good collection of containers, others have only a few and it is here you can help (with permission), by providing some vases yourself. It is also easier to arrange flowers in your own familiar containers. A useful container found in almost all homes is a baking tin, providing it is water-tight (two coats of varnish will help). This can be painted and weighted with gravel placed in the bottom; when this is filled with crumpled wire-netting it becomes a very useful container for windowsill arrangements.

It is important to find out when it is convenient for you to work in the church. Some churches are kept locked unless they are being used for a service, so you will have to find out where the key is kept. Most church flowers are changed on a Friday or Saturday morning so as to be at their best for the Sunday worship.

Whether you are a member of a team working together in a large church or cathedral, or taking your turn on a rota system, the equipment you will need to take with you is the same. A watering can with a long thin spout (for topping up the finished arrangement), containers, wire-netting, wire-cutters, floral foam, pin-holders, florists' scissors, a sharp knife, string, wire, secateurs and a bucket. A large sheet of polythene should always be used to protect the floor and surface you are working on, as all flowers should be arranged where they are to stand. The sheet can also be used to spread out the new floral material on so that it is easy to select the flowers needed. Lay them in groups of tall, medium and short flowers.

Some people do not wish to arrange flowers in church but are willing to contribute by providing flowers either from a florist or from their own gardens. Flowers should be picked the day before they are needed, either early in the morning or late at night when they are loaded with water. The stems should be re-cut under the water and any woody stem ends split. All the lower leaves that will be under the water-line must be removed. Leaves submerged in water for a long time cause bacteria to form and there is nothing worse than dead or wilting flowers in church. Stand the cut flowers and foliage in deep water in a cool and airy place. This gives them a chance to fill up with water, so allowing them to last longer.

The flowers can be left in the deep water while they are taken to the church and if the bucket or large container in which they are standing is placed in a large wooden box, this will prevent spillage if the flowers have to be transported by car.

Buckets, a watering can, secateurs, string and plastic sheeting are all useful items of equipment.

PEDESTAL ARRANGEMENTS

Many churches possess pedestals made from wood, stone, wrought-iron, gilt or brass, and these are ideal for arrangements as they are tall and allow the flowers to be seen easily from most parts of the church. A pedestal should be solid and stand firmly on the ground. It should also be capable of supporting a heavy arrangement. There is not always a matching vase for the pedestal, but any vase or bowl or large cake tin will do for an arrangement where the flowers and foliage will conceal the container, as long as it is not too deep and has a flat base so that it will fit squarely and safely on the pedestal. An urn-shaped vase is ideal when the container is intended to be visible. Gravel or stones can be placed in the bottom of the vase to give greater stability.

When two pedestals are to be used, perhaps to be placed either side of the chancel steps, the problem arises of producing two identical flower arrangements. The flowers are best divided into two matching groups before the arrangement is started. Fill the vase with crumpled wire-netting, making sure it reaches over and above the rim. Some arrangers can manage with only wire-netting in the bowl but I prefer to place a pin-holder underneath the wire, to help hold the first and tallest stems firmly in place. Others use floral foam pressed onto the pin-holder and then covered with wire-netting. Tie the whole thing, bowl as well, to the pedestal to keep it firm. This is best done with string, as wire may damage the pedestal. Having placed the bowl on the pedestal, fill it almost to the rim with water; this will stop the stems from drying out while you arrange the flowers and so help them to last longer. The vase can be topped up with water from the back when the flower arrangement has been completed.

I am often asked which flowers to choose and this, of course, depends upon whether you are buying from a florist or picking the flowers from the garden. The season of the year also determines the type of flowers available. In all cases though, try to pick some fine tall leaves or flowers for the outline, such as Gladioli, Michaelmas Daisies, Eremurus, Delphiniums and the pointed leaves of Iris or Scirpus grass (Bulrush). Although if you wish to use Bulrushes, do pick them in the green stage or before they are fully mature and spray them with artists' varnish or heavy hair lacquer to stop them bursting into fluffy seed. They can also be purchased in florists' shops. Include

These elegant twin pedestal arrangements include
Moluccella laevis *(Bells of Ireland), Gladioli and spray*
Chrysanthemums, *with added greenery and striped grasses.*

some large flowers for the centre and some medium ones for filling in. Avoid blue flowers if the background is stone, as these will not be seen from a distance. Try to pick some trailing Ivy or other leaves to swerve down over the rim of the container, which will help unite the vase to the pedestal.

Having decided whether you are going to use light or dark flowers and leaves, start by making a triangular pattern with the tallest and most pointed flowers. Aim for height at the centre. Some people find when making these large arrangements that the flowers overbalance and fall backwards or forwards. This should not happen if your first stem is placed centrally and two-thirds back in the vase. If your arrangement is inclined to topple forwards, this can be corrected by hanging a weight from the wire at the back of the vase. A piece of lead strip or a spare pin-holder is ideal for this.

After establishing the height and width with the pointed flowers, strengthen the centre line with bigger, bolder or rounder flowers. Then add some leaves low down near to the centre and finally fill in with medium flowers, working from the outside of the design to the centre, aiming all the stems to a point beneath the tallest central stems. Make sure that some of the low flowers or leaves flow forward over the rim of the vase, allowing them to protrude. This will prevent the flower arrangement looking flat. Add some shorter stems at the back, again to avoid the appearance of a flat-backed arrangement. There should always be plenty of space between the flowers in a large arrangement so that they can be seen by all the congregation. If small, closely packed flowers are used, the effect from the back of the church will be just a blob and the beauty of the blooms will be lost.

On one occasion I was asked to arrange the flowers in a country church and was disappointed to find that the church had no pedestals, only two large jugs standing either side of the chancel steps. Having been in the country the previous day I had picked flowers and foliage from the fields and hedgerows: dark green trails of Ivy, long stems of Cow Parsley or Queen Anne's Lace (I re-cut the stems under water to avoid an airlock forming in the hollow stems and so allowing for a greater intake of water), masses of Bracken (submerged in water for a few hours before it was needed to prevent floppiness) and Common Ragwort. I also picked Wild Dock for its tall spires which are so good for height and outline (tall Rosebay Willow-herb is a good substitute). The more I looked around the more I could see the potential of many of the wild flowers, but I decided to plan the arrangements using mainly yellow and white as I wanted the flowers to show up well in the dark church.

Using the same shaped material you can make a similar arrangement. Fill the jugs with crumpled newspaper, sand or gravel and put crumpled wire-netting on top. This will prevent the flowers from dropping to the bottom. Then fill the containers three-quarters full with water and make the tall triangular outline of the arrangement using the tall Dock (remove all the leaves as these make the final effect untidy). To vary the arrangement make the height of the design taller on the handled side of the jug and flowing down and out over the lip on the opposite side. Placed one each side of the chancel steps, this will give the appearance of both arrangements swerving into the centre. After the Dock, follow with the tall stems of Queen Anne's Lace, making some of the stems tilt forward, then place the Common Ragwort in between, making sure to place it further into the arrangement than the white flowers. This will make the finished effect much lighter. Ferns can be added to the back of the arrangement, although they will not show up well if the background is dark. However, Ferns do give a finish to the design and help to cover the wire-netting.

ALTAR ARRANGEMENTS

Although the altar is the focal point of a church, not all churches have flowers on their altars. This will depend very much on the denomination of the church, the reredos (the screen or wall panelling behind the altar) and the size of the altar. If the reredos is very ornate, the flowers set in front of it will not be easily seen by the congregation; a pedestal arrangement placed either side of the altar is more effective. This also applies when the altar is too small to take flowers.

Many altars have a Cross and two candlesticks on them. The most important thing to remember when designing an arrangement for this type of altar, is that the flowers and foliage must in no way detract or overshadow the Cross, nor must they get in the way of the priest when he is conducting the service. A good arrangement will lead the eye to the Cross which stands in the centre of the altar. The flowers are usually placed between the Cross and the candlesticks which stand on either end of the altar.

When choosing the flowers you will not only have to consider the reredos but also the background behind it. In some churches the colour of the altar frontal will be changed for the various festivals of the year. This will usually be white and gold for special occasions like weddings, confirmations, ordinations, the Harvest Festival and Christmas. The altar arrangements should harmonise with the altar surroundings to form one whole picture.

Altar vases are usually very beautiful but often have the disadvantage of very narrow necks which make arrangements difficult. Permission must be given before any substitute can be made. If a narrow-necked vase is your problem, you will find it easier to arrange the flowers if you first insert a plastic oil funnel into the top of the vase, filling the wider cup with crumpled wire-netting or floral foam which has been previously soaked in water. A tall stem can be inserted through the wire-netting and down through the spout of the funnel into the vase, allowing the flower plenty of water. This is important, as all altar flowers must remain fresh for up to a week. Other flowers and greenery can be tilted at angles down into the cup. Alternatively, bowls with bases which will fit snugly into the neck of the vase can be secured to the top of the vase with string or wire or adhesive clay, taking great care not to damage the vase.

Whichever method is used, the eye can be led to the Cross by making the design higher on the outside (never higher than the Cross), and swerving it down to the inside near the Cross. The flowers should never be nearer than 10 cm (4 inches) to the Cross.

For a wider topped vase, fill it with wire-netting allowing the wire to come above the rim of the vase. This allows the flowers to be placed at the side almost horizontally through the wire, but make sure that the ends of the stems turn down into the water. Make the outline of the design off-centre by placing the first tall stem to the left of the centre (for the left-hand vase), with the further stems flowing out below on the right towards the Cross. Fill in with the shorter flowers, making sure that some flow forward to avoid the flat effect often given by two-dimensional designs. Repeat the idea for the right-hand vase, placing the tallest stem to the right of the centre and making the lower left-swerve move in towards the Cross.

Always check your arrangement, as you work, by walking back to view it from the nave. This allows you to get the effect from a distance and also to check that the two arrangements are well balanced.

In a large church or cathedral there may be small individual side-chapels which will require altar flowers. As these altars will be seen at close range, a delicate and more casual arrangement than those of the main altar can be designed. Use flowers with pale and muted shades. White flowers are very suitable for chapels used for private prayer as they are peaceful and serene. Blue flowers are often used in chapels dedicated to the Virgin Mary.

WINDOWSILL AND PULPIT ARRANGEMENTS

When a church has windowsills, fine use can be made of them. Flowers look especially effective where the windows of the church let in a lot of light. Any kind of trough or a long narrow baking tin or plastic food container can be used here. These can be painted or concealed in an outer container. In a country church a basket is ideal for this. A large variety of baskets can be found in department stores and fancy goods shops at reasonable prices.

Another idea is to wrap a block of water-soaked floral foam in plastic. Tie this with string and fix it to the window ledge before inserting the flowers into the foam.

Before you arrange the flowers, check that the container stands firmly on the sill; some stone sills are not always flat. A large piece of plasticine placed between the base of the trough and the sill will hold the container firmly in place as long as both surfaces are dry. A wooden door wedge is also helpful.

A low arrangement is the most suitable for windowsills since it is important that the flowers do not block the light. Having prepared the container, insert the more pointed stems to make a low triangular pattern (the centre stem should be no higher than one-and-a-half times the depth of the trough or tin). Place the shorter, rounder flowers at the centre-front and fill in with the medium flowers, allowing some to flow over the rim of the container. Add

foliage to finalise the arrangement, making use of trailing greenery to unite the design with the sill.

Pulpits can be very ornate or very simple. They can be decorated for special occasions, such as weddings or flower festivals, and, as they are usually high, an arrangement placed under the lectern is effective. This can be made with a block of floral foam inserted into a plastic container and tied securely to the lectern. Make sure the flowers flow downwards. Alternatively, an arrangement can be placed at the base of the pulpit, or, if the pulpit is ornate in itself, an interesting emphasis can be achieved by fixing dry flowers to a strip of ribbon or velvet, allowing this to hang down as a Bible marker. The flower arrangement must in no way obscure or obstruct the clergyman when he is giving his sermon.

RIGHT: *For this beautiful font decoration, dainty pink and white flowers were interspersed with Gypsophila and massed in shallow tins filled with water-soaked floral foam.*

OPPOSITE: *This striking arrangement adds emphasis to the monument of George Monox in Cirencester Parish Church. Arrangements such as this should always complement, never overpower, a church monument.*

BELOW: *These white Lilies and Roses with grey green foliage are massed in a circular style suitable for a table in the vestry.*

Feasts and Festivals

Arranging flowers in church is always a special experience, but when there is a festival in preparation the people involved are often aware of an atmosphere of joy and tranquility.

The purpose of flower arrangements in church is not simply to please the eye with beautiful colours, shapes and forms, but to encourage peaceful thoughts and religious feeling.

It is an established practice to celebrate religious festivals, including Christmas, Easter and Harvest Festival, by decorating the church with a mass of flowers and foliage. Although certain colours are traditionally associated with these festivals, there is no rule that these colours must be seen in the flower arrangements. However, it is a pleasant gesture to follow the colour theme in the flowers. If you are in any doubt, you should always seek the advice of the clergyman.

EASTER

The forty days between Lent and Easter are a time of penitence and during this time flowers are not usually placed in churches. Later the spring flowers of Easter time are a joy to behold with all their light yellow and fresh green colourings. The flowers which are available will depend very much on what date Easter falls. This can vary from March 22 to April 25 depending on when the first full moon appears after the vernal equinox. Eastern Orthodox churches celebrate Easter a week or more later than Western churches.

The severity of the winter will have a bearing on the type of flowers which are available. A week of sunshine just before Easter will bring on flowers which otherwise might not have opened in time.

For the main arrangements on the altar and pedestals, the small flowers of early spring are not suitable, but Daffodils or Narcissi with their golden yellow trumpets, mixed branches of the winter flowering shrub Corylopsis, Hazel Catkins from the hedgerows, Lilies and Arums will make a fine arrangement.

Daffodils and Narcissi are excellent flowers for adding light and brightness to the darkest of interiors, especially if arranged with dark green shiny leaves. Cut the Daffodils when they are in bud as they will quickly open once brought inside. When Daffodils are first cut they give off a slimy sap from the ends of their stems. This should be wiped off or washed off under a tap. If this is not done the sap will seal the base of the stem and prevent the flower from taking water.

If Easter falls late and the winter has been a mild one, some of the fruit blossoms may be in flower. Cut the branches of blossom when the flowers are in tight bud as a warm room will soon make them open. If the flowerheads are removed as they die this will help to prolong the life of the other buds as they open. Blossom usually grows on graceful arching branches and an arrangement will look much more effective if only a few branches are used. If the branches are too closely packed together the natural outline of the laden boughs will be lost. Most blossom branches are heavy and must be arranged in suitably sturdy containers weighted at the bottom with stones.

Prunus is one of the most popular types of spring-flowering blossom, with a wide range of Almond, Cherry, Plum and Peach to choose from. The colours

vary from the clear pink flowers of *Prunus dulcis* (almond) to the pink-budded, opening to white flowers, of *Prunus* 'Fudanzakura'. Cherry blossom has the added beauty of deep copper-coloured leaves. Some Prunus blossom is not suitable for flower arranging as the flowers tend to hang down from the branches in pendulous clusters and these cannot be seen clearly from the back of the church. All blossom branches have woody stems and these must have the bottom ends crushed or split with a knife to allow the stem to take in water.

Tulips are a very popular spring flower which can be used in Easter decorations. Tulips first appeared in Europe in the mid-sixteenth century and have continued to fascinate gardeners and horticulturists through the ages, resulting in a tremendous range of varieties to choose from. They are grown in every colour and colour combination imaginable: red, pink, purple, white and yellow. Some are bi-coloured with speckles or stripes of contrasting and harmonious colours. They also vary in size and shape, some having short stems and some having long stems. The lily-flowered *Tulipa* 'Dyanito' has long red petals curving in around the middle with the tops of the petals forming sharp points. 'Scarlet O'Hara' is a scarlet red Tulip belonging to the Darwin group with rounded petals giving it a global shape. *Tulipa* 'Sunshine' is a parrot Tulip with yellow irregular twisted petals and frilled edges. *Tulipa* 'Orange Wonder' has scarlet shading on orange-bronze petals and belongs to the group known as Triumph. *Tulipa* 'Groenland' and *Tulipa* 'Viridiflora' are cottage Tulips growing on tall rigid stems. Their green markings make them particular favourites for flower arrangements.

Whichever variety and colour you choose, there are a few problems which can arise when using Tulips as cut flowers for flower arranging. The stems have a tendency to curl down over the side of the vase once they have been inside for a few hours and what was a beautiful arrangement when you left it, can be a limp and sorry sight the next morning. Proper conditioning after the flowers have been picked should prevent this from happening. The Tulips should be wrapped in newspaper so that the flower and the stem are well supported. They should then stand in deep water in a cool dark place for four hours before they are arranged. If, however, they do droop they should re-straighten if they are reconditioned in the same way as when they were first picked.

Another peculiarity of the Tulip is that they continue to grow in water. This means that a so-thought 'finished' arrangement may have changed overnight, thus altering the balance of your design. This will necessitate the re-cutting of the stems and rearranging the flowers.

When choosing a position for an arrangement which is to include Tulips, it is important to bear in mind that Tulips will turn to face the light. The only remedy for this is to make sure that they are not standing in direct light from a spot-light or a window. Light will also cause Tulips to open and some Tulips can measure up to 11 cm (5 inches) when they are fully open. This does not necessarily spoil a design as the centres of Tulips are usually beautifully coloured with strong contrasting colours. If you wish your Tulips to remain in their original shape keep them away from direct light and do not place them near a radiator or heater.

Small delicate-stemmed spring flowers can be included in an arrangement for a windowsill: Primroses, Violets and Grape Hyacinths can be arranged with *Narcissi* 'Actaea', with their white petals and red-edged yellow trumpets, as well as Pussy Willow and one of the small-flowered blossoms like the white Fuji Cherry (*Prunus incisa*). These flowers arranged into a moss base with tree bark make a natural and attractive display. As the container will be completely hidden under the moss, an old plate or shallow baking tin can be used. It is a wise precaution to cover the area of the windowsill which will be covered with moss with plastic sheeting as this will prevent possible damage to the windowsill. Cut the plastic into an oval shape the same size as your intended mound of moss. Place the container filled with crumpled wire-netting on top of the plastic and place the dampened moss over the container and to the edge of the plastic. Place the pieces of bark at the back of the moss and diagonally across the moss mound. The flowers are arranged into the moss, the taller stems of Narcissi, Pussy Willow and blossom form the outline of the arrangement

penetrating through the spaces in the moss so that their stems are in the water of the container. Place some Narcissi at the centre, making the stems look as if they are all coming from the same central position as they would when growing in the garden or woods. The smaller flowers are arranged into the moss in clumps so they look as if they are growing in the mossy mound. The finished effect should look as if all the flowers are in their natural habitat.

The same floral material can be used with the bark acting as the container. Line the curved inside of the bark with tin foil and then fill it with damp moss. The flowers are then arranged into the moss, placing the smaller flowers at the lower front and the longer stems at the back. If you have difficulty making these taller flowers stand up in the moss, a pin-holder can be placed under the moss and the flower stems inserted in this.

If there is a suitable position in the church where an Easter garden can be placed (perhaps in the children's corner or at the rear of the church), this can make an eye-catching scene. The garden will not only give pleasure to the congregation but also to any visitors who may visit the church during the Easter holiday. If the church or a member of the local community possesses some small biblical figures these can be incorporated in the garden.

The tomb can be constructed using rocks and stones, and a piece of calico placed in the entrance for the shroud.

The flowers must be the smallest varieties of spring flowers so as not to overpower the figures and look out of scale in the garden. Four shallow, wooden fruit-boxes glued together into one large square make an ideal base. Line the boxes with polythene and fill them with damp sand and cover it with damp moss. The sides of the box can be painted or concealed by nailing wire-netting around them and then inserting greenery into the wire. Small rocks placed at the back of the garden give a sloping elevation with boughs of blossom and Pussy Willow to give height. Clumps of Heather can make bushes, and Daffodils, Violets and Primroses can be embedded into the moss. These small flowers do not necessarily have to be cut flowers as the whole plant can be dug up from the garden and the roots placed in a polythene bag. The bag can then be planted into the moss and sand. The plants can be returned to open ground once the garden is dismantled.

Yellow and white flowers are ideal for a dark corner in the church. The arrangement, BELOW, *includes Freesias, Irises, Daffodils, Pinks, Roses and Tulips.* OPPOSITE: *Lilies, Chrysanthemums, Carnations, Pinks and Daffodils are backed with early Forsythia,* Viburnum Opulus *'Sterile' and sprays of Ivy.*

HARVEST FESTIVAL

Come, ye thankful people, come,
Raise the song of Harvest-home:
All is safely gathered in,
Ere the winter storms begin.
HENRY ALFORD

The Harvest Festival is an unofficial religious festival, to celebrate the successful gathering in of the harvest and for offering thanks for the fruits of the earth. In the Jewish church the Feast of the Tabernacles, or Feast of the Ingathering, was originally a harvest festival where booths (sukkots) were made out of branches hung with autumnal fruits and vegetables. These huts were used as dining areas or temporary living quarters.

The Christian church celebrates this festival with a thanksgiving service during which local people bring gifts of harvest fare to the church. Churches are packed with harvest gifts and arrangements are kept to a minimum so that they do not detract from the main harvest display.

The floral arrangements are more in keeping with the occasion if they are limited to the russet colours of autumn, making good use of the red, gold and tawny coloured leaves which can be found in most gardens and woods. Stalks of Bearded Wheat (*Triticum turdidum*) are always appreciated in town churches. Wheat can be bought from some florists, but if it is not available, it must be cut from the fields before the combine-harvesters set to work and can then be hung up to dry in a warm, dark place. Red

Anemones can be arranged among the corn to resemble the summer Field Poppies so often seen growing among the ripening crops.

There is a wealth of brightly coloured berries available at this time of year, including the orange and red berries of Berberis or those of the Pyracantha, so aptly called Firethorn, with long sharp thorns. It is advisable to wear strong gloves when cutting this shrub.

Rose hips are another source of material which can be incorporated into a harvest design, *Rosa moyesii* being an excellent variety with its thorny branches bearing long, shiny bright red hips, or *Rosa rugosa* having orange-red global shaped hips. Another orange fruit-bearing plant is the Chinese Lantern (*Physalis alkekengi*) with its stems hung with paper-like lanterns.

The hedgerows of autumn offer a wealth of autumnal foliage and plant material and the grey-white fluffy seed-heads on long trailing branches of Old Man's Beard, the Wild Clematis, can be twined around pillars and statues or used in any arrangement which requires hanging lengths of flora.

Fruit and vegetables do not just have to be part of the harvest display but can be combined with flowers and foliage in large pedestal or tall cone-shaped designs. Gifts of fruit and vegetables can be placed around these tall arrangements at ground level but it is advisable to have someone with knowledge of flower arranging in charge, to group them, as many people bring their offerings and just place them on the floor.

Some of the heavier fruits, such as bunches of grapes, apples and pears, will have to be wired into the container. However, this should be avoided when possible as wiring will shorten the life of the fruit. Take care when using fruits such as black grapes or cherries as these will leave a nasty stain if they shed their fruit onto an altar cloth or fabric covering in the church.

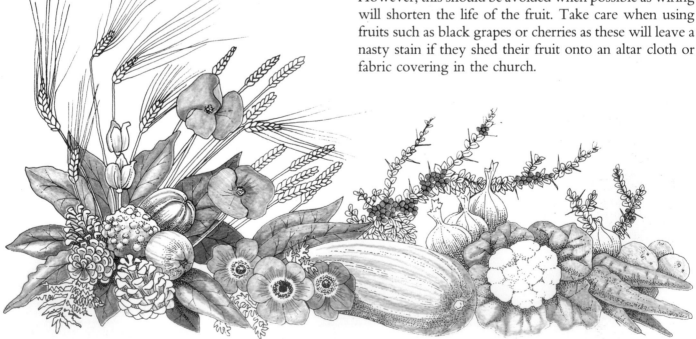

Ornamental gourds come in all shapes and sizes; some have smooth skins, others knobbly wart-like ones. The colours range from green through to orange, yellow and cream. The 'Turk's Head' gourd with its silver stripes on a dark green skin, the club-shaped, pale yellow 'Butternut' squash and the round, bright orange 'Golden Nugget' are just a few of the many to choose from. Their colours can be accentuated if they are painted with a coat of clear varnish.

Harvest arrangements look at their best if the colour of the container is harmonious with the general colour scheme of gold, yellow, orange and red. Copper vases and jugs are perfect since they reflect the rich colours of the autumnal foliage. Wooden vases and baskets are also appropriate, their neutral brown and straw colours blending in with the harvest scene. Glazed pottery, earthenware, brass, pewter and stone containers are also suitable. If you can find a farmer who will lend you a milk churn, the lid can be reversed and a bowl can be concealed inside it. This could be used for a tall arrangement suitable for standing near the church entrance or at the back of the church. Vegetables could be placed at the base.

Swags can be attached to the ends of the first two pews or tied around pillars or columns. Dried materials lend themselves well to swags and can be built into the design well in advance of the Harvest Festival.

You will require a mixed collection of dried leaves, flowers, nuts, gourds and cereals. The leaves should be large and flat so that they form a background for the other dried materials. Common Laurel or the glorious dark burnished Copper Beech are perfect.

The brown and sepia-coloured, elongated or short and thick cones from the Pine tree or the Spruce cones with their elliptical or cylindrical shapes are very suitable for building into swags. Ripened Ornamental Corn can be purchased from shops selling dried flowers and grasses. 'Strawberry Corn' is global in shape and has deep red-coloured kernels. The variety *Zea mays* 'Japonica' includes tinges of pink and red in its otherwise pale yellow

kernels. Peanuts and chestnuts are easier to wire than some of the other harder-shelled nuts and add small dashes of beige-brown to the swag.

There are no set rules as to what material should be built into a swag, it depends very much on the choice of the individual.

The swag will need a base onto which it will be built; this can be made from a 5 × 2 cm (2 × ¾ inch) length of wood, nine 6 cm (2½ inch) nails, three polythene-covered blocks of floral foam and some wire-netting.

Hammer the nails through the length of wood so that the spikes protrude at one side. Place the nails in groups of three, set at equal distances apart. Press the polythene-covered foam blocks onto the nails and wrap wire-netting around them to hold them firmly to the wood and nails. The dried material is then inserted into the foam, keeping the main weight of the swag in the middle and top blocks. Use the large flat leaves to make backgrounds for the heavier material.

Large fir cones will have to be wired before they can be used and this is done by winding stub wires round the lower section of the cone. These are then twisted together at either side and bent down to meet beneath the cone where they are twisted into a stem. Gourds, soft-shelled nuts and cobs can be wired in a similar way, but the wire must be first pushed through the sides. Try to taper the bottom of the swag using pointed and elongated shapes of dried grasses, leaves or small cobs.

The finished swag can be tied or wired into position or hung on a nail if there is one already in the church. Never hammer your own nails into the fabric of the church.

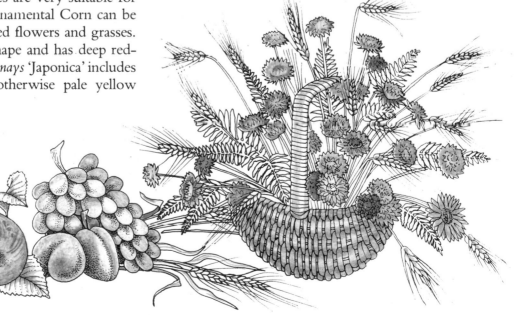

87

Vegetables not only make delightful decorations grouped together or incorporated in an arrangement, but can also make unusual containers. Pumpkins are ideal for this; the large pale orange, globe-shaped pumpkin is suitable for large arrangements and the smaller, bell-shaped ones for smaller designs on side tables.

To use a pumpkin as a container, slice the top off it and scoop out the soft flesh inside. Line the hole with aluminium foil or polythene and fill it with water-soaked floral foam. Flowers and foliage can be arranged into this. A design made from branches of brown leaves, copper and bronze Chrysanthemums and dark green foliage arranged in a pumpkin container makes an unusual windowsill arrangement. Branches of berries can also be included in the design and the shiny black berries of the evergreen Privet make a good contrast against the orange skin of the pumpkin. Some of the stems can be arranged so that the berried clusters hang down over the edge of the container. Remember to split the bottom of the stems of woody-stemmed flowers and shrubs before arranging them.

It is not only for swags that dried material can be used. There is a wide range of plants to choose from, but it is best to keep to the less exotic varieties for Harvest Festival decorations. Teazles, dried Poppy seed-heads, stems of wheat, oats and barley will all fit in well with the harvest theme. The flat, bright yellow, dried flower-heads of Yarrow can add a splash of colour to an arrangement made from neutral shades of brown.

Dried leaves and cone-laden branches will look very effective incorporated with shiny berries and a few fresh flowers. Fruit and vegetables can also be used with pressed leaves, fresh flowers and dried grasses.

A point to remember, when mixing fruit with fresh cut flowers, is that the fruit must not be allowed to rest on wet floral foam or moss, which is essential to cut flowers. This can be avoided if the fruit is pierced with a cocktail stick and the other end of the stick inserted into the foam base. A larger stick can be used if greater height is required. Oranges, apples, limes, lemons and gourds can all be arranged using this method.

This corner rectangular design for a harvest festival is composed of autumn leaves, berries, Chrysanthemums and wheat, with the addition of fruit, vegetables and bread. The container is a long baking dish filled with blocks of floral foam pressed onto a large pin-holder for stability. The sprays of Larch cones were placed first to establish height and width. Old Man's Beard (Wild Clematis) was also included and the fruit and vegetables were grouped along the ledge. The lower leaves and cones flow forward to avoid a flat effect.

CHRISTMAS

The holly and the ivy,
When they are both full grown
Of all the trees that are in the wood
The holly bears the crown:

This is the time of year when the leaves and branches of evergreen shrubs and trees are used in profusion to decorate churches for the Christmas services held to celebrate the birth of Christ throughout the Christian world. Flowers are expensive at this time of year and there is not the wide range to choose from as in the spring and summer months, but a few Carnations and Chrysanthemums can add an attractive splash of white, yellow or red among the greenery.

Holly and Ivy were used in pre-Christian times and considered to be plants with magical powers to ward off evil. The Christian use of Holly and Ivy for Christmas decorations was probably a continuation from the ancient custom of gathering greenery at the time of the winter solstice. This greenery was used in rituals to ensure the crops and vegetation returned the following spring.

To prevent church arrangements from appearing too green, include some of the variegated foliage of Holly, Aucuba, Euonymus and Ivy in the arrangements. *Hedera canariensis* 'Variegata', known as 'Gloire de Marengo', has large leaves with dark green centres which are surrounded by silver and edged with pale cream. The Common Ivy (*Hedera helix*) includes among its varieties one of the finest golden Ivies, named 'Buttercup' or 'Golden Cloud', and 'Marginata' has a green-blue centre with a cream edge which has a pink tint in the winter. Flower-bearing Ivy

can often be found clinging to trees in the country or in the hedgerows and the domed flowers, which are made up from a mass of round umbels, can be sprayed gold so that they stand out against the shiny green leaves.

Holly, usually chosen for its clusters of bright red berries, can also be found with variegated leaves, and the silver-edged leaves of 'Argenteo-marginata' or 'Ferox Argentea' with spines of pale cream can be used with great effect in an arrangement of mixed foliage. Artificial Holly berries can be added to the leaves if necessary.

The Christmas Rose (*Helleborus niger*), as its name suggests, can be found in gardens in December onwards and has been grown since the sixteenth century in England. An arrangement of these white saucer-shaped flowers in a side chapel or included in table or altar arrangements is not only beautiful but ideal for the setting. Before you arrange the flowers, drag a pin down the stems and leave them in deep water with a little sugar added.

Various shades of green can be brought into the church by including stems or branches of Hemlock, Yew, Spruce or Pine. Many of these will have cones on them, which will look particularly attractive if flicked with white paint or artificial snow. It is advisable to wire the cones in place as they have a tendency to fall when they are brought into a warm environment. The foliage of evergreens, such as Mexican Orange (*Choisya ternata*), the Spotted Laurel (*Aucuba japonica*), *Skimmia japonica* and *Viburnum tinus*, is also very useful.

As always, before deciding on your Christmas designs, the interior of the church must be taken into account. Think carefully when using gold- or silver-painted foliage, as this will be lost if the church has ornately painted screens or an intricately carved reredos. The use of frosted or painted foliage should be used sparingly so that the natural beauty of the foliage and flowers is not lost. In many old churches beautiful candle sconces can be found, and circlets of greenery and flowers can be hung from these. Red ribbon adds a festive touch.

Pedestal arrangements will look magnificent standing either side of the chancel steps using variegated Holly with pale yellow-edged leaves, white or yellow Chrysanthemums, trails of Ivy and green Holly with masses of red berries. The red of the Holly berries will complement the greens of the arrangement and accentuate the yellow edges of the variegated Holly.

If the interior of the church is reasonably warm, pots of Poinsettia (*Euphorbia pulcherrima*), commonly known as the Christmas Flower, can be arranged around the base of the pulpit, the bright green leaves and scarlet flowers fitting in well with the other Christmas arrangements of Holly, flowers and greenery.

Weddings

When you are asked to arrange flowers for a wedding, the first person you should consult is the bride. She may be only too happy to leave the choice of flowers and the positioning of the arrangements to you, but if she has definite ideas as to what she would like, you should visit the church together and discuss the possibilities.

The main points to consider are the interior of the church, the colour of the bride's and bridesmaids' dresses and bouquets and also the personality and appearance of the bride. A small, petite bride will be completely overshadowed if the church flowers are too large and there are too many of them, whereas a taller, more sophisticated, bride will be complemented by bold and spacious arrangements. The permission of the clergyman must be obtained before the final decision is made on the placing of the flower arrangements.

White flowers are traditional for a wedding and look particularly effective when incorporated with fresh green foliage. Lime branches in flower, stripped of their dark green leaves, make a beautiful background for white Lilies and cream Roses. If the bride is to be dressed in white and carry an all-white bouquet, flowers which tone with the bridesmaids' dresses can be very effective. For a wedding which is held in the summer, stately Delphiniums with their wide range of purple and blue spikes, pink Roses and Peruvian Lilies (*Alstroemeria*), with their irregular trumpet-shaped flowers, will form an interesting group. Be careful though, when using predominantly blue flowers, for these tend to fade into the background and can appear almost grey in dark interiors. If blue flowers have to be used, some light-coloured foliage, placed with them, will show the flowers up to better advantage. Alternatively, a spot-light can be focused on the flowers.

If the bride has a particular variety of flower she wishes to have in the church it is wise to check with your florist to see that these will be available. Most florists can order flowers which they do not usually carry in stock, but if this is not possible they will be able to recommend a good substitute in colour and shape. Availability will depend very much on the time of the year but, whichever flowers are decided upon, remember to place your order well in advance of the wedding.

Wedding flowers are best arranged the day before the ceremony, allowing the arrangements to settle overnight. They can then be checked the following morning, the containers topped up and any necessary repairs carried out. It is always advisable to keep a few flowers in reserve from your original floral material for this purpose.

Positioning It is important to remember that the flower arrangements must be able to be seen by all the congregation and not just the bridal party. During the marriage ceremony the congregation will be standing up most of the time and so the flowers must be shoulder height so that they can be appreciated by everyone.

Flowers are not always placed on the altar but, when they are, it is best to use the church altar vases as some wedding flowers are removed immediately after the service and this ensures that the altar is not left bare. Pedestal arrangements are ideal for weddings and can be placed either side of the choir stalls or chancel steps, remembering when arranging the flowers that four people will have to be able to stand comfortably in this area. They can also be placed in suitable corners or at the rear of the church.

The font, which is usually near the main entrance, can make an exceptionally attractive base for an arrangement and flowers can either be placed around it or placed in a water-filled container in the basin of the font (permission must be gained before you do this). The porch is another place which can be decorated; flowers can be placed on the porch bench or a hanging decoration can be suspended from the roof to welcome the bride to church.

In large, spacious churches good use can be made of windowsills, but care should be taken in small churches

not to give the appearance of overcrowding. Simplicity is the main aim of the flower arranger.

PEW END DECORATIONS

Decorated pew ends are only suitable when the church has a wide aisle; flowers placed on the end of pews may interfere with the bridal procession as it passes up the aisle. Designs should not extend beyond the sides of the pew as these may obscure the pew entrance, nor should they protrude too far into the aisle.

There are many methods of decorating the ends of pews: some decorations can be hung from the top of the pew, others can be made in a low tin or plastic bowl, rising up in a tapered form from floor level. An easy but very effective method is to place narrow troughs or plastic food containers at floor level, filling these with short flowers and greenery. Stones or something weighty should be placed in the base of these low containers before filling them with wire-netting or floral foam, otherwise they may tilt over.

Any type of pew end decoration you choose to make can be made at home, having first checked how many you will need. On many occasions the aisle will look better if only every other pew carries a decoration. The finished designs can be put in their places a few hours before the ceremony when you will be going to the church anyway to check the other arrangements.

The type of pew decoration you decide to make will depend upon the style of the pew, but a great deal of trouble can be saved if you order in advance a number of special holders filled with floral foam from the florist. To save on expense, a suitable alternative can be made from a strip of wood with a hole drilled in the top which can be hung with wire, string or ribbon. Hammer a few nails into the back of the wood so that they protrude the other side, and onto the nails press some blocks of water-soaked floral foam. Cover the whole with polythene, using a double piece at the base to catch any drips. Finally tie the foam to the wood with string or floral tape. Insert string or ribbon in the hole at the top and hang the swag from this. Insert short pieces of greenery first, followed by the flowers, finishing at the top with a fuller spray of flowers and at the bottom by some more pointed stems. If it is difficult to insert the stems through the thin polythene, make holes with a knitting needle first, or, better still, only cover the bottom with polythene.

BELOW: *A glowing decoration for the end of a pew to brighten a dark church.*
OPPOSITE: *Masses of Daisy-spray Chrysanthemums and clouds of Gypsophila are combined in these beautiful pew decorations for a wedding.*

A further idea is to use a long shallow plastic food container. Make a hole at the top through which to insert the hanging string, then fill the container with wet floral foam, holding it firm with elastic bands, string or tape. The longest flowers should be inserted pointing downwards, the rest can be placed 'in' and 'out' finishing, if you like the idea, with a cloud of Gypsophila. Cow Parsley or Queen Anne's Lace also give a light effect; in fact the whole decoration can be made with these simple country flowers. This idea would look particularly pleasing if finished at the top with apple green or pale pink ribbon bows.

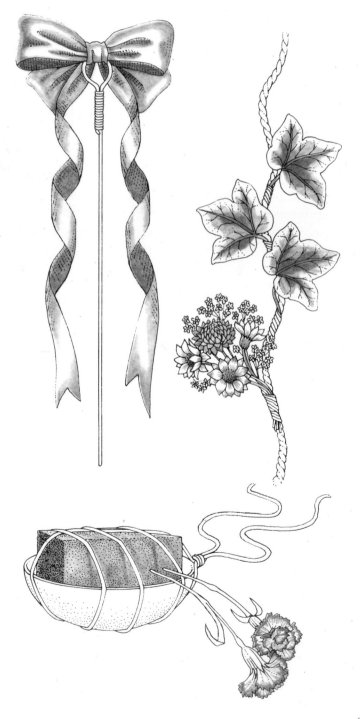

When your design incorporates the use of ribbon bows, these will need to be attached to wire before they can be inserted. Bend a length of wire over to form a loop, rather like a hairpin, then pass the ribbon through this loop and tie it in a bow or a simple knot for a streamer. To make the ribbon streamers curl, drag the ribbon between thumb and knife blade, pressing hard against the blade. Not all ribbons will do this, but if using satin ribbons, you can wrap this round a cylindrical object and hold it over a steaming kettle. When dry the ribbon will assume a curl.

If you wish your pew end decoration to have a 'tail', this can be made separately using mossing string. Cut the string to the correct length, allowing extra for attaching the tail to the holder. Twist a length of Ivy around the string, anchoring it to the string with reel wire, where necessary. Add small, delicate sprays of flowers, binding the stems with reel wire and leaving a length of wire at either end to bind the flowers to the string. Place the flowers at regular intervals along the string, making smaller and smaller sprays and finishing with a trail of Ivy.

Finally attach the finished tail to the holder and check to see that the main part of the arrangement and the tail unite well, and that the holder is not visible.

WEDDING PEDESTALS

If you require greater height in your pedestal arrangement than the tallest stems in your floral material can give you, metal or plastic florists' cones can be attached to wooden sticks or garden canes with wire or adhesive tape. Hold the cone in place against the stick and wrap the wire or tape around the cone and the stick until the cone is held firmly in place. To secure the wire, grasp the two loose ends together in a pair of pliers and twist the pliers clockwise. Keep twisting until the cone is secure.

Fill the metal cones with wet floral foam and insert the stick through the wire-netting in the main container. If you have no cones, a good substitute can be made from 15 cm (6 inch) lengths of floral foam and polythene bags. Place a piece of water-soaked floral foam into one of the bags, leaving the top of the bag open. Attach the bag to the stick with adhesive tape in the same way as for a metal cone. Whether using cones or the above substitute, three of these set in the centre of an arrangement will give considerable lift to the main line of your pedestal design. Arrange the taller central flowers into these, filling in the outline and centre of the arrangement with shorter-stemmed flowers and foliage. Check when you have finished to see that none of the metal cones or polythene can be seen between the flowers and foliage.

ARRANGEMENTS FOR A PORCH

A basket arrangement In a country church the porch will often have a bench inside it where a flower arrangement can be placed. This is a welcoming sight for both the guests and the bride before they enter the church.

A basket is an ideal container, with an immense range to choose from – varying in texture and colour as well as shape and size. They are usually made from cane, willow, reeds or palms and the shape will depend upon what the basket was originally intended for. Some will have handles and some will have lids. It is important to consider these as the handle must be incorporated with the flower arrangement. Florists sell baskets which are specifically designed for flower arranging as they have a plastic or tin container inside them. These are ideal – but remember when choosing that many of them have high arched handles which will require a lot of flowers and greenery; and what appears to be a small basket can, when filled with flowers, become a large, spacious arrangement and completely unsuitable for the position for which it was designed.

A basket without a special lining can have a plastic bowl, a shallow dish, or a baking tin placed inside it, depending upon its size and depth. The container should not show above the sides of the basket and can be held firmly to the base of the basket with a piece of adhesive clay. The container can be filled with floral foam or crushed wire-netting and larger baskets, such as cut-flower-baskets, can have extra wire-netting placed over their openings and secured to the sides of the baskets with reel wire. A small, closely woven basket can be lined with polythene and the floral foam put directly into the lined basket. This method is not suitable for open-weave baskets as the polythene will show through between the weave.

Choose your basket with care, considering carefully the colour and the size of the porch as well as the bench itself. The size of the basket will have a bearing on the choice of flowers. A basket which is the correct shape and size but the wrong colour can always be painted with emulsion paint.

The flowers will have to unite with the flowers in the church, but blue can be used as a predominant colour, even if it has not been used much inside the church, since the flowers will only be seen at close range. If the bench is made from dark wood, pale yellow or white flowers included in the arrangement will help to accentuate the richness of the blue flowers. A background of cool-looking pale yellow-green leaves, such as Honeysuckle, or Lady's Mantle (*Alchemilla mollis*), incorporating light green leaves with yellow-green flowers, will show up well against a dark background.

Flowering Fennel (*Foeniculum vulgare*) with its feathery, thin, filament-like leaves and tiny yellow flowers borne in flat umbrella shapes is also useful here. Cat Mint can be found in most gardens and is good for outline, having pale blue flowers and pale grey-green leaves. The main blooms in such an arrangement could be blue Hydrangeas if the basket is big enough to take the large corymbs (the leaves of Hydrangeas can also be used). Scabious, sometimes called the 'pincushion flower' because of its protruding centres, adds pretty mauve blooms held at the end of slender stems. Clematis offer a wide range of purple and blue flowers depending on the month of the year (these are good for trailing over the sides of the basket). Cornflowers have erect purple, blue and pink flowers, a new variety, 'Blue Diadem', having extra-large flowers – these, too, can add emphasis to your colours and arrangement.

Once you have chosen your floral material, study the shape of the basket. Most baskets will fit in well with a triangular pattern for an arrangement, remembering that the handle of the basket must not be completely hidden by the flowers and foliage. Start by placing the tallest stem of a delicate flower in the centre of the basket so that it is fractionally higher than the handle; next, place two long stems of the same type horizontally at the sides so they reach over the sides of the basket. Place a shorter spray either side between the centre and the side flowers, keeping within the outline of the triangle. Place the larger single blooms in the centre and down near the front edge of the basket, then fill in from side to side and top to bottom with smaller flowers and foliage. Make sure that some of the flowers are set deeper into the arrangement than others to avoid a flat effect. Finally leave the porch and return a few minutes later to check that your arrangement of flowers looks attractive to anyone entering the church.

A hanging decoration These are ideal where the porch has no bench. They can be suspended from the ceiling or roof of the porch providing it is high enough to allow the guests to pass freely under it. A floral foam ball is suitable as the base for a hanging decoration. Cover the ball with Sphagnum moss (found in woods or purchased from florists or garden centres) and bind this to the ball with string, leaving long ends by which it can be hung in the porch (these ends can be bound with florists' tape if they will be visible).

The hanging ball will look most effective if the main

flowers are interspersed with smaller flowers. If the two varieties are to be the same colour, try to choose varieties with different textures. Smooth flowers reflect light and rough textures absorb it, so by mixing rough and smooth a good contrast is achieved. Cut the stems of the flowers so that they are shorter than the radius of the foam ball (the distance from the centre of the ball to the outer edge) but not too short or they will not be held firmly in the ball. If the stems of the flowers are not strong enough to push into the foam, make a hole in the ball with a fine knitting needle or bodkin before putting the flower in. If this is necessary you will need both hands free – so push the ball down onto a knitting needle until it is in the centre of the needle. Place the ball in the centre of a cardboard box with the ends of the knitting needle resting on the edges of the box. When half the ball is filled, turn the ball over and continue to fill the other side. Holding the ball by the loose ends of string, pull out the knitting needle and insert two flowers into the holes left behind. Streamers and bows can be added in the same way as described for a pew end decoration.

BOUQUETS AND HEAD-DRESSES

Brides' and bridesmaids' bouquets are best left to the professional florist but a simple head-dress for a very young bridesmaid can be made at home. Very delicate flowers should be used and sometimes these will need to be wired before they can be inserted into the head-band. Wiring is used when extra strength is needed for an existing stem or to provide a stem for a flower or leaf which does not already possess one – this is called mounting.

The following methods of mounting and wiring can be adapted for most varieties of flowers, but good wiring takes practice and patience and is strictly florists' work. Wire is sold in different thicknesses (gauges); the lower the metric gauge, the thinner the wire, the higher the imperial gauge, the thinner the wire. Two kinds of wire are used for wiring, stub wire which is sold in lengths which vary from 18 to 46 cm (7 to 18 inches) and reel wire which is

sold on a reel. The gauge or type of wire you use will depend on the weight and proportion of the flower, but all wiring should be kept as light as possible. Stub wires are usually used for the stem of a flower or leaf and reel wire for binding, unless the flower is particularly delicate and then only reel wire is used. Florists' tape is used for covering the wire stem.

Leaves

The leaves should be conditioned well before they are wired by leaving them soaking in deep water for several hours. Take a single leaf and trim the stem so that it is very short. Cut a piece of reel wire which is double the length of the required finished stem, plus double the length of the leaf. With the front of the leaf facing you, pass one end of the wire through the leaf from the back to the front approximately two-thirds down from the top of the leaf and close to the central vein. Bend the wire into a hair-pin shape and pass it back through the leaf close to the central vein exactly opposite the original insertion. The bend in the wire lies across the central vein of the leaf. Wind one piece of wire around the other, starting at the base of the leaf and making sure to combine the real leaf stem between the wires. Finish the false stem by binding it with florists' tape.

Single Flowers and Florets

Single flowers Flowers that are needed to stand upright or forward facing in a head-dress or similar decoration, can be wired in the following way. Trim the flower stem to the required length (which will depend for which purpose it is to be used but for a head-dress trim it to 2.5 cm (1 inch) making sure the stem is straight). Choose a stub wire which is slightly thinner than the stem. Bend the end of the wire over to make a hook and then thread the wire through the top and down the stem until the hook is embedded in the centre of the flower. Do this very gently so that you do not tear the delicate flower petals.

Florets This method of wiring is used for single florets which have been taken from a flowering spike made up of small individual florets (such as Delphiniums and Hyacinths or when the flowers are delicate and tubular, bell or trumpet shaped). Remove the florets from the main flower stem trying to leave some length of stem wherever possible. Pass a length of reel wire through the stem, near the base of the floret. Twist the two ends together at the base of the floret taking care that the stem does not split where the wire is inserted. Cover the lengths of wire with florists' tape to make a stem.

OPPOSITE: *Small 'pot trees' make stunning table decorations for a wedding reception or special occasion. This one is covered with white Roses, Lady's Mantle (*Alchemilla mollis) *and Rosemary sprigs.*

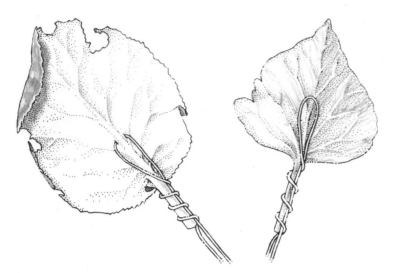

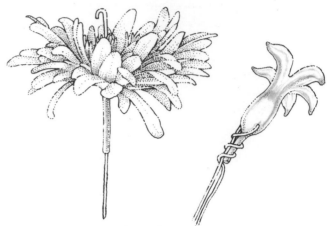

LEFT: *Individual leaves are threaded with reel wire, which is then wound around the short stem. Delicate leaves are given support by a loop of wire on the underside.*

RIGHT: *Single flowers with a hollow stem are given support with a length of reel wire. Single florets are threaded with wire, which is then twisted at the base.*

Simple Bouquets

Very young bridesmaids look charming if they carry a flower ball or flower basket instead of a large bouquet. Make the flower ball from a foam ball hung with ribbon and cover it with pastel-coloured flowers, such as short Chrysanthemums, Pinks and Carnations.

Alternatively, flowers can be arranged in a small-handled basket. Attach a tin to the inside of the basket with adhesive clay, then fill the tin with water-soaked floral foam before inserting the flowers.

The Bridesmaid's Head-dress

Measure around the bridesmaid's head where the head-dress will lie and add 2.5 cm (1 inch) to this measurement. Cut a length of 0.90 mm (20 gauge) wire to this length and bend 1 cm (½ inch) over at one end to make a hook and the same amount at the other end to make a loop. To keep the loop in place, bind the end of the loop to the main wire with reel wire and then cover the whole band with florists' tape, binding it at an angle so that it overlaps. Mark the centre front of the band with a small mark. Divide the flowers you are going to use for the head-dress into two equal groups. Working from the back to the centre front, taking care that the band does not twist as you work, bind the flowers and leaves to the head-dress with florists' tape. Make sure that the main flowers face straight out from the band and not up or down. The flowers can get larger nearer the front of the band but this should be gradual, not a sudden jump from tiny flowers to a large central bloom. Make sure that the head-dress is symmetrical. The band is fastened into a circle with the hook and eye.

A very simple but extremely pretty head-dress for a young bridesmaid can be quickly made using a needle and cotton. Select a velvet ribbon to match the bridesmaid's dress, about 2.5 cm (1 inch) wide and long enough to tie round her head. Sew a few short-stemmed fresh flowers to the band at the front. The ribbon can be worn like a hairband and tied in a bow at the back.

WEDDING RECEPTIONS

The reception party after a wedding ceremony is usually held in a hotel, hired hall or at home. The flower arrangements at a hotel will, unless you specifically ask to do the flowers, be provided by the management, but in halls and at home the flowers will have to be provided and their arrangements organised by the florist or the bride's family. Forward planning is essential as there are several things to be considered before actually arranging the flowers.

The style of the wedding reception will play an important part in the selection of the flowers and the size and placing of the arrangements. At a formal reception the guests will be sitting down at tables and the size of the tables will affect the type of floral design chosen. Long trestle tables will look best with one centrepiece arrangement and two smaller ones placed at either end of the table.

Small individual tables call for a delicate centrepiece on each of them. One problem this produces is finding a large number of matching containers and it is sometimes best to use saucers with blocks of floral foam taped or wired to them. The flowers are then inserted into the foam with the longer-stemmed flowers placed near the saucer rim and lying horizontally to the table top. Make sure that they do not interfere with the place settings and fit in well with the colours of the tablecloths and napkins. Table arrangements should never be too tall as these will obstruct the guests' view of the main bridal table.

If the reception is a buffet all the guests will be standing most of the time and here the arrangements must be high and tall so they are not hidden by the guests. One important thing to remember, whatever the style of the reception, is that the flowers should make a strong impression on the wedding guests, and usually a few large arrangements will be more eye-catching than many small ones placed low.

As always, when selecting flowers, the interior of the hall or house must be considered. Often the reception flowers will follow the same colour scheme as those for the wedding ceremony.

The bride welcomes and greets her guests as they arrive at the reception and here one large pedestal arrangement is perfect, providing there is sufficient space, as the arrangement should be seen over the heads of the bridal party. Try to place the flower arrangement in a position so that it does not interrupt the flow of guests.

If the wedding reception is to be held at home, space is often at a premium and a marquee may be hired to get over this problem. Decorating a marquee is a challenge for any flower arranger and it is best to have more than one person involved.

The canvas of the marquee is often off-white so this rules out the use of white and cream coloured flowers so popular for weddings, as they will be lost against the canvas. Some marquees have striped linings and the colour of the stripes will have a bearing upon the colour scheme of the flower arrangements.

Marquees come in all shapes and sizes but most of the larger ones have interior poles holding them up. These poles are often unsightly and can be decorated with garlands of foliage and flowers or strands of Smilax. The flowers and foliage should be wired to a main wire with reel wire and then the garland can be twisted around the pole with the ends held in place with a staple or nail driven into the pole.

LEFT: *Floral foam held in position with wire-netting.*
RIGHT: *The finished 'pot tree' covered in flowers and foliage.*

An arrangement either side of the marquee entrance is a welcoming sight. Pedestal arrangements can be used here, but take great care to anchor them steadily, as the ground is often uneven and they may be knocked over.

Home-made 'pot trees' can look just as effective as pedestal arrangements and are more secure. To make these you will need two large flower pots or tubs, two dowel sticks or straight branches sharpened at one end (straight branches are better since they are covered in bark which makes them look more natural), some large stones, blocks of floral foam and wire-netting.

Place the unsharpened end of the pole in the centre of the flower pot and place stones or bricks around it so that it is held firmly in a vertical position. Cover the stones with soil and moss. Wire several blocks of floral foam together. Cut the corners off with a sharp knife until the mass of foam is a rounded shape. Press the foam onto the sharpened top of the pole and cover it with wire-netting. Large blooms can now be inserted into the foam with variegated or pale green foliage or smaller flowers placed between them. Continue until the whole surface of the floral foam is covered.

Floribunda Roses are one of the many flowers which are suitable for a 'pot tree', and the large blooms of 'Iceberg' mixed with the yellow green flowers of Lady's Mantle (*Alchemilla mollis*) are a good combination.

Small 'pot trees' can be made in the same way, and these make striking table decorations. Ribbon streamers inserted into the flower ball are a finishing touch. (See illustration page 99.)

The interior of a marquee being high and spacious can take immense and exotic arrangements. These can either be placed in the centre of the marquee or around the sides, providing they are firmly anchored to the ground. Large arrangements can be made by using florists' cones wired to a stick which is then placed in the main container. The flowers are arranged in the cones, giving extra height to the design.

Another effective way of decorating a marquee is to have arrangements hanging from the roof. The lower flowers of a hanging decoration must not be too low (you must allow for the guests passing underneath them), equally the decorations should not be too high or they will not be noticed. The size of the arrangement will depend on the size of the marquee and it is advisable to ask the tent erectors to leave lengths of rope hanging from the top of the tent to which the finished hanging arrangements can be attached.

Open wire or plastic mesh baskets, used by nurserymen for hanging patio baskets, come in a variety of sizes and make ideal containers. Wire lampshade frames are also very effective. Place a block of water-soaked floral foam in the base of the basket, setting it on a base of moss or polythene to avoid any drips. This is not always necessary, for if you have placed the foam aside until the drips have ceased, it will hold enough moisture for the duration of the reception. Insert the flowers pointing upwards, outwards and downwards to form a round sphere. Start with perhaps short greenery, then add the medium length flowers and finally insert the longer ones protruding outwards. Keep your flowers light, not only in weight but in colour also – mauve and blue flowers do not show up well in a marquee. A colour scheme of yellow, white, coral and

Lilies, Roses, Spider Chrysanthemums, green Viburnum opulus *'Sterile' and leaves of Eucalyptus are combined in this fine mantelpiece arrangement.*

green is an ideal combination; although a pink colour scheme is often popular in summer when there is such a wide variety of pink flowers available. Pink Asters, Pyrethrums, Sweet Sultans and Godetias are ideal for the inside, whilst longer flowers, such as Larkspur, Clarkia, Sweet Peas, spray Carnations and even the pink Scabious are ideal for the outside. To obtain a light effect, insert some of your short-stemmed flowers 'in' and some of the longer-stemmed flowers 'out'.

If you do not use a basket, you can use two or more blocks of floral foam wrapped up in wire-netting. Such a sphere filled with Daisies and Gypsophila looks enchanting, and made with pale Pinks and White Heather, they can be left to dry and still look lovely after months.

Some marquees are rather daunting at first sight, so as well as using hanging baskets, you could try making a cascade to hang down from the top portion of one or more of the poles. To do this, wrap two or preferably three bricks of floral foam in wire-netting, and hang these one below the other on nails previously hammered into the pole. Insert a burst of flowers into each block so that they almost join each other, adding trails of Ivy or Honeysuckle or Periwinkle to form a cascade. One large pedestal group can be placed at one end of the marquee, or two large 'flower trees' stood at the entrance.

Christenings

Flower arrangements for a Christening service should be kept very simple and confined to the font and the area around it. The word 'font' is derived from the Latin word for 'stream', dating back to when the baptism ceremony called for total immersion in water. The font is usually situated near the main church entrance and will vary in shape and structure depending on the age of the church. Some fonts are made from lead but these are rare and it is more usual to find them carved from stone or marble.

In many old churches the font is the only original piece of Norman furniture to have survived through the centuries and is usually square or circular in shape. Octagonal fonts did not appear until the late fourteenth century. These lent themselves to the elaborate carvings so popular in the fifteenth century, each face of the octagon being carved and often depicting the Seven Sacraments of the Church and the crucifixion.

Most fonts stand on some form of pedestal or on one or more steps and will have a flat rim around the outer edge of the bowl. These are the features that can be decorated with flowers to give the best effect. When arranging flowers around the upper edge of the font it is important to allow plenty of space for the priest to conduct the ceremony without being restricted in any way by the floral decorations.

Some churches will have special containers which are used around the edge of the font but this is seldom the case and a good base can be made from polythene and floral foam. Sew or glue a long thin strip of polythene together, along the longest edge, to make a narrow sleeve tube which will fit three-quarters of the way around the upper edge of the font. Fill the long sleeve tube with pieces of water-soaked floral foam and seal the ends with adhesive tape. Attach this firmly to the font with adhesive tape. If a single frontal arrangement or several separate arrangements are more in keeping with the design of the font, individual polythene-covered blocks of foam can be attached to the font in the same way.

The flowers for Christenings should be small and delicate. Shades of blue and white or pink and white are the most popular choice, although other pastel shades can be used, especially when there is to be more than one Christening on the same day. For a spring Christening, Snowdrops mixed with Scillas are very pretty, or White Heather with Cupid's Dart for the summer. Pink Viburnum among the Snowdrops will not only add a pink tinge for a girl's Christening arrangement but if *Viburnum fragrans* is used, its rich scent will fill the church. When using small flowers, such as Snowdrops or Scillas, try tying several stems to a toothpick and inserting this into the polythene.

Apple blossom makes a beautiful sight around the top of a font, with its delicate pink flowers and darker pink buds, but remember to pick it when it is not in full bloom to ensure that it will not lose all its petals as soon as it is brought inside the church.

Having selected your flowers and foliage, arrange them around the polythene ring, pushing the stems through the polythene into the foam. If you find it difficult to insert the stems through the polythene, pierce it first with a fine knitting needle. Allow some of the foliage to trail downwards over the outer edge of the font, and make sure the polythene cannot be seen through the flowers and greenery of the finished arrangement. The ends of the tube can be finished with a pink or blue ribbon streamer which has first been attached to a piece of wire. This can be made at home beforehand.

If the font does not have a flat rim where flowers can be placed, the polythene tube can be tied around the outside of the font close to the top, and secured with adhesive tape.

An alternative to this is to string together a number of empty meat-paste jars and tie these around the top of the font. The jars can then be filled with Primroses or similar short-stemmed country flowers with Ivy twisted around the string to conceal it.

A square font can look very attractive with three small arrangements placed at the corners, leaving one corner free where the priest will stand to conduct the ceremony. These arrangements should not be too tall or they will obscure the guests' view and detract from the beauty of the font. The containers should combine with the stone or marble of the font and should not be too deep; china or even plastic dishes would be suitable. These can be secured to the font with adhesive clay placed between the base of the container and the top of the font.

If the font is of a very simple design with perhaps a simple unadorned bowl standing on a single column, flowers can be entwined around the under edge of the bowl and spiralled down the pillar. For this type of arrangement you will need 0.90 mm (20 gauge) wire, florists' tape and reel wire. Measure around the outer edge of the bowl and around the pillar following the line where the finished garland will be placed. Cut the wire to the correct length and cover it with florists' tape, winding it diagonally around the wire so that it overlaps itself and covers the wire completely. If the flowers are too small they will not be seen among the foliage – a medium bloom like the *Chrysanthemum leucanthemum* with its yellow centre and white petals is ideal. Alternatively, small flowers can be grouped together and the stems bound with reel wire. The single flowers or posies should be placed against the main tape-covered wire at regular intervals, and bound to it with florists' tape, binding around the stems and main wire to form a garland. Make sure that the flowers face forward, not up or down. Trails of Ivy can be twisted around the wire between the flowers and secured with reel wire where necessary. The flower-covered wire can then be wrapped around the font and pillar securing the ends to the font with adhesive tape.

Although formal flower arrangements are not suitable for Christenings, a single arrangement on the far edge of the font can look charming, as long as the flowers are delicate and natural in appearance. Honeysuckle picked when in full bloom or Escallonia, with its slender arching branches of rose pink flowers and small bright green leaves, are very suitable. Purple, pink and white Sweet Peas with silver-grey foliage arranged in a bread basket which has been painted white are an ideal combination.

CHRISTENING RECEPTIONS

When planning designs for a gathering after a Christening service, rather simple flowers are called for. The flowers should be pink, blue or pastel shades. If the church font was decorated for the Christening service, the flowers for the party should be the same colour. The vases should be unsophisticated, such as white china, cherub-vases or basketware cradles. These look delightful filled with Forget-me-nots, Polyantha Roses, which are grown in a variety of different colours, and small pink Chrysanthemums. Suitable varieties of Chrysanthemum would be either 'Portrait', which grows in sprays, or the small blooms of the pompon Chrysanthemum 'Fairie'. The delicate star-shaped Gypsophila can be added to these flowers as a filler.

When planning the party, the Christening cake must be considered as well as the flower arrangements as this will be a focal point on the buffet or tea table. If a small arrangement of flowers is placed on the cake, these should harmonise with the arrangements in the room. Bowls of sugar almonds can also be placed around the room as their pastel colours blend well with Christening flowers.

One charming gesture which is always pleasing to the guests at a Christening party is the Continental custom of presenting each of the guests with a small bag of sugar almonds, a symbol of the coins and gratuities distributed by the godfather at Christenings in earlier times.

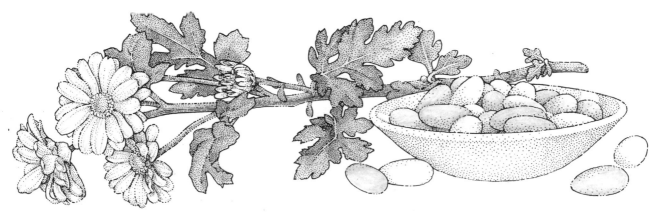

THE FLOWER ARRANGER'S GARDEN

A flower arranger can practise, indeed excel, at the craft, without ever cultivating a garden. It is very likely, however, that as his or her interest develops the opportunities offered by a garden of one's own will become more and more desirable. Ownership of a garden widens enormously the choice of plant material, making the creative possibilities for flower and foliage arrangement almost infinite. Furthermore, material can be picked at the optimum moment. Less tangible advantages should not be overlooked: flower arranging and gardening are complementary crafts; the flower arranger can only gain in artistic sensitivity by observing the line and form followed by plants growing in the soil, illuminated by natural light, while the gardener whose eye is especially keen to appreciate a shapely bloom or leaf form will have a lovelier garden to show for it.

Planning the Garden

The use of the term 'garden' to describe what is under consideration here is important: the aim is to achieve a place which is attractive in itself as well as furnishing interesting material of high quality for flower arrangement.

When designing your garden, whether from scratch or if reshaping an established plot, try to make it labour-saving as far as possible. This means limiting the number of plants that need a lot of attention in the way of tying in, staking or clipping to shape. A certain number of tall plants are essential, however, and a good way of supporting them is to put in a few canes grouped in a circle and strengthened with twine early in the season while they are low-growing. The mature plants will hide the supports.

Wooden trellises for climbers look charming, but need regular treatment with preservative or paint if they are not to rot and need replacing altogether. Fine plastic netting is durable and climbers weave in and out of it very easily, doing away with the need for tying in. Oddly enough, black netting is far less obtrusive than the bright green kind.

Shrubs and hedges that need constant trimming furnish little material to the flower arranger, though hedges gen-

erally make more effective windbreaks and better-looking boundaries than walls, which can create frost pockets. A slow-growing informal hedge is the answer: Escallonia is a good choice, which even thrives in seaside gardens, and flowers profusely in June and July. Fuchsia, Forsythia, Rhododendron and, of course, the Rose, are other possibilities.

Ease of access to plants is important in all gardens, but in none so much as the flower arranger's. Do not make borders so wide that you cannot comfortably reach all the occupants. If necessary, leave space for a narrow path at the back of the border. Alternatively, dot random stepping stones amongst the plants, but take care they do not become havens for snails, slugs or insect pests. Island beds, especially for Rose bushes, are ideal, but there is not always enough space in modern gardens. Smooth comfortably wide paths are essential and look best if a slight curve, off-centre, rather than a perfectly straight line, leads the eye to a focal point such as a rustic seat or piece of statuary. Prefabricated concrete slabs or York stone, if available, are good materials. Brick paths have a pleasing appearance and can easily be made to any shape, but green algal growth may form and make the surface slippery. A tar-oil wash should be applied if this occurs.

Flowers for cutting used to be banished to the vegetable patch, where their regimental rows matched the cabbages for dreary neatness. Few of us are willing to sacrifice that amount of space these days, though there is something to be said for consigning short-lived flowerers such as some bulbs to a distant corner where, stripped of their glory, they can die down out of sight.

Make provision for a paved area, however small, near the house, preferably enjoying some shade. With a simple table and bench, it will not only be useful for outdoor entertaining, but will be a place where you can contemplate the garden scene, leisurely working out plans for the garden itself and for arrangements comprised of what it has to offer.

Choosing what plants to grow is both exciting and difficult. Since in temperate zones the choice is astonishingly wide, it makes sense to be as well-informed as possible in order to avoid disappointing failures. To discover what will thrive in a particular garden it is necessary to identify two factors: the character of the site and the type of soil.

Canes are required to give firm support to Delphiniums.

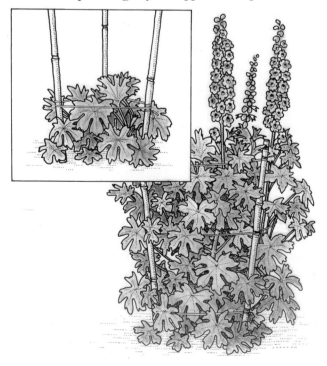

Site Draw a plan of the site on graph paper. A simple outline drawn to a workable scale of, say, 3 mm:30 cm (⅛ inch:1 foot) will serve. Mark on it the aspect of the garden and any walls that enclose it; note down the prevailing wind, and any particularly open or sheltered areas; insert permanent features such as mature trees, in the shade of which a limited range of plants will be happy, or architectural features such as statuary, paving and steps. Indicate the direction of sloping land, if relevant, as this will affect the variation in efficiency of soil drainage from one part of the garden to another. A basic plan like this can be used year after year when working out bedding schemes and as more information is added annually it becomes a garden biography of great value.

Soil type Having established whether the garden is sunny or shaded, open or sheltered, look at the soil. Working the ground for a year or two is the best way to get to know what type of soil you have. The chart below sums up briefly what you are looking for.

Kind of soil	Characteristics	Disadvantages
Sandy	Open texture; light to work; quick drainage; well aerated; slightly acid. Warms up early in season	Nutrients easily washed away; dries out quickly
Loamy	Dark, friable, moist but well-drained	
Clay	Highly water-retentive; cold	Difficult to work; heavy when wet, hard when dry
Chalky	Thin; quick-draining	Chemical activity of lime deprives plants of some essential nutrients

All soil types benefit from the annual digging in of well-rotted organic matter – farmyard manure, garden compost, spent hops, mushroom compost – to improve the texture and build up the humus content which nourishes plant life. Sandy and loamy soils can use a top dressing of general fertiliser annually in spring at a rate of 50 g/m² (2 oz per sq. yard) for sandy soils, half as much for loam.

Lime Sandy soils may need a dressing of ground limestone at 75 g/m² (3 oz per sq. yard) every third autumn if they become too acid – you will know this is happening if plants that normally flourish show obvious signs of undernourishment because potash and phosphate have been leached away. Since lime greatly improves the texture of clay soils it can be applied more liberally, say at 100 g/m² (4 oz per sq. yard) every other year until the texture is more agreeable.

Lime is a powerful substance and should be used with care. Use ground limestone or hydrated lime, never quick lime; delay the application of lime until at least two weeks, preferably a month, after dressing with fertiliser or manure. It is always best to test for lime requirement first.

The degree to which lime is present in the soil will affect the available choice of plants. The following will not grow in a limy soil: Rhododendrons and Azaleas, Camellia, Gaultheria, *Eucryphia glutinosa*, *Skimmia fortunei*, species of Erica (except *E. carnea*), Calluna, Vaccinium, Grevillea, Kalmia, Pieris and some Lupins. Calluna, Azaleas, Camellias and Grevilleas may, however, be grown in pots of suitably enriched soil (incorporate peat and/or leaf mould).

Eucryphia glutinosa, *Rhododendron, Kalmia, Pieris, Calluna and Erica will not grow in limy soil.*

Drainage In soils that are clearly sandy in type, water drains away fast; in heavy clay, it seeps away slowly. Neither situation is a healthy one for plants, the roots of which need not only the nutrients contained in water but also air, which will be in suffocatingly short supply in a waterlogged soil. If you are not sure how good the drainage is in your garden, dig two or three holes at various points of different levels. The holes should be about 60 cm (2 feet) deep. See how long the water takes to drain away after heavy rain. If the holes are still full after two or three days, drainage is bad and should be put right. The remedy depends on the cause. If the trouble is that for years the topsoil only has been cultivated, leaving a hard compressed pan beneath, double digging the land (i.e. digging it two spits deep) should do the trick. If clay soil is to blame, lime should be incorporated as described above; if the worst happens and the water is trapped at a deep level, drains (earthenware pipes) may have to be laid.

Choice of Plants

Favourable subjects One of the most enjoyable ways of finding out what will do well in your area is to visit local show gardens open to the public, where you will get a host of ideas for planting schemes as well as reliable information about suitable plants. Nearer at hand, take a look at neighbouring gardens: what thrives there is an excellent indication of what you too can expect to succeed with. Make friends with local fellow-gardeners and with the nearest nurseryman, who will be happy to advise you. The annual catalogues of reputable seedsmen are full of ideas and information and make fireside reading in January as stimulating as any novel.

Colour The choice is so broad it may be difficult to know where to start. Working to set colour schemes is a good way to get going. Pink and crimson flowers throughout the season will be supplied by Paeonies, Larkspur, Sweet Peas, Dahlias and Roses. Yellow variations may be gained from Daffodils, Doronicums, Columbines, Rudbeckias and the exquisite climber *Clematis orientalis* with its delicate leaves and bobbing star-like flowers. For blues and violets no garden can afford to be without Delphiniums, while Grape Hyacinths, Gentians, Love-in-a-mist and Canterbury Bells extend the range. The background colour to gardens and arrangements alike is of course green. In addition to plants with good foliage, such as Choisya, Viburnum, Hosta and Spotted Laurel, include some Euphorbia for their shapely bracts, and for green flowers use Love-lies-bleeding (*Amaranthus caudatus* 'Viridis'), *Helleborus corsicus*, Bells of Ireland (*Molucella laevis*), and Lady's Mantle (*Achemilla mollis*).

Shape and size Amongst plants useful for their height are Eremurus, Foxgloves, Delphiniums, Alstroemeria, Coreopsis, Gypsophila, Phlox, Solidago and Pyrethrum. Since some need staking, it is advisable to limit the selection to those you have time to care for. Seeking out plants which have an unexpectedly attractive feature – such as the seed-boxes of Rudbeckia, Love-in-a-mist, *Clematis tangutica* and Honesty – or that have an unusual shape can become a fascinating obsession. Eryngium, Dicentra, Crinodendron and Allium spring to mind.

Everlasting flowers Most everlasting flowers can be grown from seed and need no special treatment other than picking them before they are fully mature, then hanging them upside down in small bunches in a dry, well-ventilated room. Try *Limonium sinuatum*, available in many shades, annual Helichrysums, the dainty pink and white *Acroclinium roseum*, Yarrow (*Achillea*), Cupid's Dart (*Catananche caerulea*) and Verbena.

Grasses Ornamental grasses are easy to grow and, some might say, essential flower-arranging material. *Briza maxima*, commonly called Pearl Grass because of its nodding heads, is a great favourite and most effective sprinkled with glitter at Christmas. Canary Grass (*Phalaris canariensis*), with its violet tint, and Cloud Grass (*Agrostis nebulosa*) are particularly useful for dry decorations.

Ferns Invaluable for shady parts of the garden, ferns make a perfect foil for flowering plants. Hardy Maidenhair (*Adiantum venustum*), Male (*Dryopteris felix-mas*), and Christmas (*Polystichum acrostichoides*) are among the most useful hardy ferns. For the greenhouse or home try Asparagus (*Asparagus plumosus*) or Sword (*Nephrolepis cordifolia*).

Weeds

It is a commonplace that a weed is simply a plant that is growing in the wrong spot. It is unwelcome, however, not only because its appearance interferes with the gardener's well-laid plans, but also because it is likely to be invasive, unsightly and greedy, so that if it does not smother cultivated plants it will starve them to death. Such invaders should be dispatched as soon as they appear. As far as possible regular hand-weeding or weeding with a hand-fork is to be preferred, but recourse to chemical weedkillers may be necessary. If there is a large area to clear before work on laying a garden can begin, use a non-selective (total) weedkiller such as sodium chlorate, diquat and paraquat or glyphosate. In an established garden, pre-emergent weedkillers based on simazine, if applied in spring, will discourage germinating weeds for months. Use diquat and paraquat against annual and perennial weeds in borders. Powerful systemic weedkillers are effective and if in gel form can be applied directly to the offending weeds with a brush without risk of damage to nearby ornamental plants.

Half-way between weeds and cultivated plants is a group containing wild flowers and plants noted for their invasive tendencies. They can be useful in larger gardens where an unpromising corner can be left 'wild' to supply foliage and some flowers at times when the garden proper is less productive. Yellow Archangel (*Lamium galeobdolon*) and its relatives are good examples of this type; Creeping Jenny (*Lysimachia nummularia*), Periwinkle (*Vinca* spp.), and Foam Flower (*Tiarella cordifolia*) are others.

A well-stocked flower garden in spring time is an endless source of delight. After the dull winter months it offers the flower arranger a splendid choice of colour and form.

PESTS AND DISEASES

Insect pests cannot be eliminated, but they must be controlled. They disfigure or kill plants by laying eggs on them, eating them, and by infecting them with disease. The following brief list describes the most common insect pests.

Insect pest	Plants affected	Treatment
Aphids	Annuals, perennials, shrubs. Young growths are distorted, leaves and stems fouled.	Spray with malathion or nicotine. Colonies in protected places, e.g. under leaves, should be treated with systemic insecticides (dimethoate or formothion).
Capsid bug	Dahlias, buddleia, forsythia, hydrangea. Leaves are tattered, buds and growing points destroyed, developing flowers deformed and discoloured.	Spray with gamma-HCH, malathion, nicotine or permethrin.
Caterpillar	Many plants are affected, their leaves eaten away.	Remove by hand and/or spray with trichlorphon, gamma-HCH or derris.
Cutworm	Herbaceous plants. Stems are eaten through at soil level and the plant collapses.	Dust soil with diazinon or bromophos.
Earwig	Chrysanthemums, dahlias and clematis suffer most. Leaves and petals eaten away.	Keep garden free of debris. Spray pirimiphos-methyl or trichlorphon on and around plants.
Eelworm	Herbaceous plants. Leaves and flowers discoloured; infested plants usually die.	Difficult to treat. Burn affected plants and avoid growing susceptible species.
Leafcutter bees	Roses and other shrubs. Semi-circular holes cut out of leaves.	Find and destroy the bees' nest – likely to be in decaying wood or old brickwork.
Leafhoppers	Roses, pelargoniums, primulas. White streaks on leaves with insect skins left on undersides.	Spray with malathion, gamma-HCH, derris, or a systemic such as dimethoate.

Good garden hygiene is essential in controlling pests. Do not let debris of any kind accumulate to provide nests not only for insects but also slugs and snails. Lay metaldehyde or methiocarb bait if these are troublesome. Garden damage may also be caused by birds, which can be partially controlled by scaring devices. Protect plants with netting, seedlings with criss-cross black cotton threads. This last system may also be used to deter cats, who love to dig up newly cultivated soil. Whatever the problem, act quickly before the pest proliferates and numerous plants are damaged. If spraying with chemicals, choose a dull, windless day.

A clean, tidy, well-tended garden is a must if disorders and diseases are to be kept to a minimum, as sturdy plants are better able to resist attack. The disorders and diseases most likely to occur are listed below.

Disease	Plants affected	Treatment
Blackspot	Roses. Dark brown or black spots on leaves which turn yellow and drop.	Spray young leaves with benomyl, mancuzeb or specific proprietary chemical and continue throughout the season.
Botrytis (Grey mould)	All plants. Fungus disease shows as fluffy covering on leaves.	Burn infected parts. Spray with mancuzeb or thiram. For bulbs, remove infected specimens and soak the remainder in benomyl.
Chlorosis	A disorder showing as yellow patches on leaves. Wisteria, rhododendrons and hydrangeas grown on chalk may suffer.	If due to alkaline soil, add sequestered trace elements or dig in peat.
Fusarium wilt	A fungus attacking in particular carnations, pinks and sweet peas that are cultivated on the same patch year after year.	Rotate crops. Sterilise soil if bad outbreaks occur. Destroy affected plants.
Gladiolus dry rot	Crocus and freesia corms may also be affected.	Discard all affected bulbs and corms. Soak healthy specimens in benomyl after lifting and inspect regularly during storage.

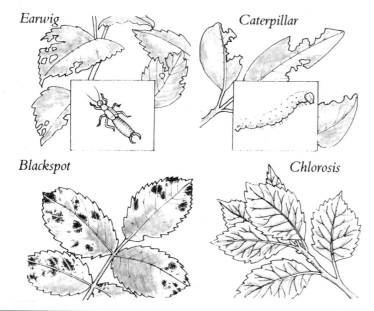

Earwig

Caterpillar

Blackspot

Chlorosis

Disease	Plants affected	Treatment
Lilac blight	In spring, young shoots turn black and wither.	Cut back to healthy tissue and spray with Bordeaux mixture.
Lily disease	A fungus affecting stems and leaves in wet seasons.	Spray fortnightly with Bordeaux mixture.
Mildew	This term covers a wide range of fungus diseases that disfigure many plants, particularly roses.	Prevent by good cultural conditions. Remove and burn affected parts, spraying with dinocap in spring and summer.
Rust	A fungus causing brown or black spots on leaves. Antirrhinums particularly susceptible.	Remove and burn affected leaves. Spray fortnightly with thiram or mancozeb. Grow rust-resistant varieties.
Tulip fire	A severe fungal disease especially troublesome in cold wet weather. Whole plant rotten and mouldy.	Destroy affected bulbs. Soak in benomyl. Spray young plants with thiram or mancozeb.
Virus diseases	Most plants are susceptible to one or another virus disease. Any part can be affected and distortion results.	Destroy affected plants. Grow only certified virus-free stock. Propagate only from healthy plants. Maintain good garden hygiene.

CULTIVATION AND PROPAGATION

Raising plants from seed

Annuals are the plants most usefully obtained in this way. They can be bought in the flowering season as bedding plants for instant colour, but this is expensive and the range on offer is likely to be limited. Growing successfully from seed is easy and rewarding. An excess of plants is likely to result, so it is a good idea to share with other gardeners.

Indoors Sow seed in pots or pans of proprietary seed compost. Garden soil will not do – it is likely to harbour harmful bacteria as well as weed seeds. Put a layer of drainage material such as clean broken crocks at the bottom of the container. Almost fill it with compost and water with a fine rose until thoroughly and evenly damp, not sodden. Spread the seeds thinly or place evenly according to size. Sprinkle over a thin covering of compost and water again. Cover with a sheet of glass, then brown paper and leave in a place where the temperature is steady at about 18°C (65°F). Check regularly to remove drops of condensation from the glass. When two or three seedlings appear, remove the covering and let them have good light. Keep the compost moist. Do not let them become drawn and spindly in the hope that by keeping them covered for a day or two longer more seeds will come up.

As soon as the first pair of true leaves appear, or when the plants are large enough to handle, transfer them to 7.5 cm (3 inch) pots of John Innes No. 1 Potting Compost, handling the plants by the leaves, never the stems, which are easily damaged. If you have a lot of plants, it is usually more practical to prick them off into seedboxes. Expose the plants gradually to outdoor conditions before planting out into their final positions.

Outdoors Ideally, many plants should be raised in a prepared seed bed and transplanted when sufficiently mature. In practice the space for this operation is not always available and seed is sown direct into the flowering site. In either event the soil should be prepared by thorough weeding, forking and hoeing to bring it to a crumbly texture and levelled out without compacting it down. Straight lines may be kept by tying pieces of thin string to small sticks firmed into the ground. Some species will need the protection of cloches to help them germinate. When the seedlings are large enough to handle, thin them out to prevent overcrowding – transplant the thinnings immediately or discard them. Do not leave them lying on the ground to attract pests or encourage diseases.

Planting out When setting plants out, aim to give them as smooth a transition from pot to ground as possible. Prepare a planting hole of sufficient size with a trowel. Remove the plant from the pot by upturning it into one hand, keeping the roots and the growing medium – compost or soil – around them intact with the other. Put the plant into the prepared hole. Refill with soil to the same depth as before and firm down well with your hands so that the plant is snug. Water in well.

Trees and shrubs

Depending on the plant's size, it may be useful to have assistance with this task. The first essential is that the planting site is well prepared, as it is going to nurture the shrub or tree for many years. Dig the spot over thoroughly a month before planting and incorporate plenty of well-rotted manure, compost or leaf-mould as appropriate.

Make a planting hole the right size. If the shrub or tree has bare roots plant as soon as you can, spreading the roots out evenly and carefully before replacing the soil, firming down and watering in. Plants with a ball of earth clinging to the roots should be set in the hole without disturbing the root system. Plant all shrubs and trees to the same depth that they were at the nursery. This will be clear from the mark of the soil on the stem. Young trees will almost certainly need to be supported by a stout stake, and this should be firmly knocked into the planting hole *before* the tree is put in. After the soil has been replaced, attach the tree to the stake either with a proprietary tree strap and buckle, with a piece of rubber inserted between tree stem and stake, or strips of hessian fixed figure-of-eight fashion for security and to prevent the tree rubbing against the stake and damaging the bark. After planting water well over the whole rooting area. Keep the area moist with a mulch of well-rotted compost or peat.

Do not plant trees and shrubs in adverse weather conditions – that is, when the ground is sodden after heavy rain or frozen hard.

OPPOSITE: *A glorious display of Darwin Tulips against a background of Prunus 'Chirotae'.*
BELOW: *Azaleas suit small borders in a shaded part of the garden.*

Planting bulbs

Most bulbs will be content on any well-drained soil, if the site is sunny. Prepare the plot by digging it over to clear away weeds and stones and then incorporating well-rotted compost. Make the planting hole with a trowel or dibber and drop the bulbs in with the pointed end up, and any old roots at the bottom. As a rough guide, plant the bulb as deep as its own size. Bulbs that have to be lifted after flowering – because they cannot survive the cold, such as Gladioli, or because the ground is required for a different planting scheme – should not be disturbed until the foliage has died down. Lift carefully with a fork and dust off the soil.

Discard any bulbs showing signs of disease. Detach any offsets. Dust bulbs and offsets with a fungicide and store in a box in a dry, cool place till planting time.

PLANTS FOR A YELLOW AND WHITE COLOUR SCHEME

Name	Height	Season	Colour
Climbers			
Clematis orientalis	up to 6 m (20 ft)	Aug–Oct	pale yellow
Lonicera tragophylla	up to 6 m (20 ft)	June–July	golden yellow
Shrubs			
Rosa 'Frühlingsgold'	2.1×2.1 m (7×7 ft)	June–Sept	pale yellow
Rosa 'Nevada'	2.1–2.4×2.1–2.4 m (7–8×7–8ft)	June–Sept	white flushed pink with yellow stamens
Perennials			
Delphinium 'Butterball'	1.3–2 m (4 ft 6 in–6 ft)	June–July	creamy-yellow
Delphinium 'Moerheimii' (Belladonna strain)	1.1–1.3 m (3 ft 6 in–4 ft 6 in)	June–July	white
Helenium autumnale 'Butterpat'	1 m (3 ft)	Aug–Sept	rich yellow
Pyrethrum 'Avalanche'	1 m (3 ft)	June	white
Lupinus 'Blushing Bride'	1 m (3 ft)	May–July	white
Oenothera missouriensis	10–15 cm (4–6 in)	June–Aug	pale yellow
Trollius 'Canary Bird'	60–75 cm (2–2 ft 6 in)	May–June	pale yellow
Kniphofia galpinii	50 cm (20 in)	Sept–Oct	soft orange-yellow
Bulbs			
Crocosmia crocosmiiflora 'Solfatare'	60 cm (2 ft)	July–Sept	apricot-yellow
Tulipa 'Athleet'	38–50 cm (15–20 in)	April–May	white
Narcissus 'Tresamble'	38 cm (15 in)	March–May	cream
Leucojum aestivum 'Gravetye Giant'	60 cm (2 ft)	April–May	white
Crocus chrysanthus 'Zwanenburg Bronze'	7.5 cm (3 in)	Feb	bronze and yellow

PLANTS FOR A SHADED SPOT

Name	Season	Type	Flower colour	Height
Astilbe	Summer	Perennial	pink/red/white	60 cm–1 m (2–3 ft)
Bergenia	Autumn/Winter	Perennial	pink	30 cm (12 in)
Cimicifuga	Autumn	Perennial	white	1.2 m (4 ft)
Cyclamen	Autumn/Winter	Bulb	pink/white	15 cm (6 in)
Digitalis (Foxglove)	Summer/Autumn	Biennial	pink/purple	1.2 m (4 ft)
Eranthis (Winter Aconite)	Winter	Bulb	yellow	10 cm (4 in)
Fothergilla	Autumn	Shrub	*leaves:* red/yellow	2×1.2 m (6×4 ft)
Galanthus (Snowdrop)	Winter/Spring	Bulb	white	7.5–20 cm (3–8 in)
Helleborus (Christmas Rose)	Winter/Spring	Bulb	yellow-green	60 cm (2 ft)
Hosta	Summer	Perennial	white/pink/lavender	60 cm–1 m (2–3 ft)
Primula (Polyanthus)	Spring	Perennial	red/white/pink/blue	15 cm (6 in)
Symphoricarpos (Snowberry)	Autumn	Shrub	*berries:* white	2×2 m (6×6 ft)
Thalictrum	Summer	Perennial	deep pink	1 m (3 ft)
Trollius	Summer	Perennial	yellow	60–75cm (2–2ft 6in)

COMPACT PLANTS FOR A SMALL GARDEN

Name	Season	Type	Colour	Height
Campanula carpatica	Summer	Perennial	blue	23–30 cm (9–12 in)
Centaurea moschata (Sweet Sultan)	Summer	Annual	white/pink/purple	60 cm (2 ft)
Cyclamen neapolitanum	Autumn/Winter	Bulb	pink/white	15 cm (6 in)
Dianthus (Pink)	Summer	Perennial	pink/red/white	25–38 cm (10–15 in)
Doronicum	Spring	Perennial	yellow	60 cm (2 ft)
Gentian	Autumn/Spring	Perennial	blue	38–60 cm (15–24 in)
Geum	Summer	Perennial	red/orange/yellow	60 cm (2 ft)
Gladiolus tristis	Spring	Bulb	cream	45 cm (18 in)
Helenium	Autumn	Perennial	yellow/red	1.1 m (3 ft 6 in)
Heuchera	Summer	Perennial	pink/red/white	45 cm (18 in)
Iris reticulata	Spring	Bulb	blue/purple	10–20 cm (4–8 in)
Kniphofia galpinii	Autumn	Perennial	red/yellow	50 cm (20 in)
Muscari botryoides	Spring	Bulb	blue/white	20 cm (8 in)
Oenothera missouriensis	Summer	Perennial	yellow	15 cm (6 in)
Phlox	Summer	Perennial	cream/rose/purple	38 cm (15 in)
Rudbeckia (Black-eyed Susan)	Summer	Perennial	gold	30 cm–1 m (1–3 ft)
Solidago 'Goldenmosa'	Summer	Perennial	yellow	1 m (3 ft)

The Spring Garden

BULBS

Look at the catalogues of specialist suppliers to discover the surprisingly wide range of bulbs available though not in general cultivation.

Daffodil *Narcissus* spp. Though not the first flower of the season, it is the daffodil that symbolises spring. The colour range extends from deep golden through clear yellow to creamy pink. *N. triandrus albus* (Angel's Tears), height 8 cm (3–4 inches), cream-white, nodding flowers with swept-back petals. 'February Gold', height 20-38 cm (8–15 inches). The *N. tazetta* group has several flowers on each stem.

Grape hyacinth *Muscari armeniacum, M. botryoides*. Deep blue, tight cone-shaped bunches of flowers borne on erect stems. Height 20 cm (8 inches). A white variety is also available.

Iris *Iris reticulata* hybrids are charming dwarf plants, 10–20 cm (8 inches) high. 'J.S. Dijt', reddish purple; 'Joyce', sky blue with a reddish spot on the fall; 'Royal Blue'; 'Violet Beauty'.

Snowdrop *Galanthus nivalis*. The richer the soil, the taller Snowdrops grow – from 7.5 cm up to 20 cm (3–8 inches).

They will grow quite happily under trees.

Snowflake *Leucojum* spp. Similar to the Snowdrop, but the small white flowers are rounder and the stems much longer. *L. aestivum* 'Gravetye Giant', height 60 cm (24 inches) is a favourite. *L. vernum* flowers earlier and is only 20 cm (8 inches) high.

Tulip *Tulipa* spp. Once the 'Royal Flower' of Turkey, the Tulip has enjoyed devoted attention for centuries, with the result that a breathtaking variety of colour and form is now available. Amongst the early singles, height 15–38 cm (6–15 inches), and their crosses, 'Athleet', pure white, 'Mon Trésor', yellow, 'Proserpine', deep carmine pink and 'Red Giant', scarlet, are outstanding. Double early-flowering varieties include the large 'Schoonoord', white, 'Vuurbaak', scarlet, 'Electra', deep cherry-red and 'All Gold'. Try to find a spot for the dwarf species such as *T. kaufmanniana* (not suitable for cutting). The variety 'Golden Earrings' is a gorgeous red outside, deep yellow within. The old cottage tulips are, sadly, not seen so much now, perhaps because of their size – up to 1 m (3 feet). Amongst this group is the valuable 'Viridiflora' type, green, large-flowered and with a pleasing rounded form. 'Groenland' is green edged with pink, an exceptionally useful combination – and eye-catching in an arrangement.

PERENNIALS

Bergenia Indispensable in arrangements for its large, glossy evergreen leaves, which are excellent for ground cover. Those of *B. cordifolia purpurea*, height 30 cm (12 inches), are tinged with purple, the drooping bell-like flowers mauve.

Bleeding Heart *Dicentra spectabilis*. Height 45–75 cm (18–30 inches). This plant is attractive as much for its grey-green frond-like foliage as its pendent rose and white flowers blooming on arching racemes in late spring.

Doronicum Popularly known as Leopard's Bane, the lasting qualities of Doronicums recommend them as much as their height (60 cm/24 inches) and their clear, yellow, daisy-like flowers. *D. plantagineum* 'Harpur Crewe' is a good choice with blooms up to 7.5 cm (3 inches) across.

Hellebore *Helleborus corsicus*, height 60 cm (24 inches), bears cup-shaped, slightly drooping yellow-green flowers. The interesting leaves are evergreen, heavy and divided into three lobes. Lasts well.

Polyanthus *Primula polyantha* hybrids. Height 30 cm (12 inches). The velvety texture of the flower petals, in a wide range of rich colours, makes a pleasing contrast with the crinkly tender leaves. The 'Pacific' strain includes blue, yellow, red, pink and white.

Euphorbia *Euphorbia polychroma* is a sub-shrubby species (height 45 cm/18 inches, spread 60 cm/24 inches). Evergreen, the leaves are bright green, the 'flowers' (bracts) bright yellow. A useful bushy addition to spring arrangements providing a highlight wherever it is placed.

TREES AND SHRUBS

The dimensions given below are for mature plants, and are approximate guides since the ultimate height and spread depends to some extent on cultural conditions. When planting shrubs from the nursery, bear in mind what their ultimate space requirement is likely to be.

Amelanchier *Amelanchier canadensis*, 3×3 m (10×10 feet), is an easy and rewarding tree to grow. Covered in racemes of pure white flowers in spring, it is perfect for spring arrangements. Its black summer berries are edible and its autumn foliage a spectacular russet. No pruning is required.

Broom *Cytisus* spp. *C.* x *praecox*, 1.5×1.5 m (5×5 feet). This vigorous shrub is generously clothed in tiny cream-white flowers borne on numerous sprays. It provides excellent coverage in the garden and is particularly suitable for mixed border planting.

Camellia Graceful nobility marks the evergreen Camellia, with its glossy dark leaves and large cup-shaped blooms. Give it a sheltered spot where it can spread up to 1.8 m (6 feet) or more. *C. japonica* varieties include 'Adolphe Audusson', scarlet, 'White Swan', white with yellow stamens, and 'Gloire de Nantes', double flowers of rose-pink. The hybrids *C.* x *williamsii* are outstanding, particularly the deep pink 'Donation'. The evergreen foliage is also valuable in decoration.

Cercis *Cercis siliquastrum* (Judas tree). If a sheltered spot in full sun is available, this species will decorate it generously. Reaching up to 6 m (20 feet), when mature, it bears deep pink flowers on the leafless twigs in spring. Flat green seed-pods of summer turn red when ripe. Plant in autumn or spring on any good soil.

Corylopsis *Corylopsis willmottiae* is a small tree – up to 3 m (10 feet) – of the Witch-Hazel family. Its racemes of pale yellow flowers against bright green leaves have an essentially spring-like charm.

Davidia *Davidia involucrata*. Known as the pocket-handkerchief tree because of the effect of the large white bracts surrounding the insignificant flowers, this deciduous tree is easy to cultivate in any reasonably fertile, moist soil. Plant from autumn to spring in sun or partial shade. The dimensions of a mature specimen will be height 5.5–7.5 m (18–25 feet), spread 3–5.5 m (10–18 feet).

Flowering Currant *Ribes* spp. *R. sanguineum*, height 1.8–2.7 m (6–9 feet), spread 1.5–2.1 m (5–7 feet), is the

A spring border of Wall Flowers, Narcissi and Doronicums against a background of Kerria japonica.

Rhododendron.

most popular species of this hardy deciduous shrub. The deep rose-red flowers are carried on long pendent racemes. Useful in spring arrangements where an element of warm colour is needed.

Forsythia This easily grown shrub is useful in town gardens and may be used for hedging if the variety *F.* x *intermedia* 'Spectabilis' is grown. 'Lynwood' has very large yellow flowers on long arching sprays. Height and spread 2.4 × 2.4 m (8 × 8 feet).

Kerria *Kerria japonica*, 1.5 × 1.5 m (5 × 5 feet). Medium-length sprays with bright green leaves bear their fluffy button-like orange-yellow flowers at the tips. 'Pleniflora' is the best-known variety.

Lilac *Syringa vulgaris*. Height 2.4–3.6 m (8–12 feet), spread 1.5–3 m (5–10 feet). Often overlooked by gardeners because it grows so commonly in town gardens, the lilac is still beloved by flower arrangers. There are many varieties offering medium-length stems with panicles of fragrant flowers: 'Massena', deep purple; 'Maud Notcutt', white, the flowers held proudly above the foliage, and 'Firmament', light lavender, are just three. Several different varieties in one garden look marvellous and offer endlessly versatile material. The race known as Canadian hybrids are very vigorous and marked by the size of the panicles – in the case of 'Virgilia' 23 cm (9 inches) long, and lilac-purple in colour.

Magnolia *Magnolia* x *soulangeana*. It is worth growing a Magnolia for the unfailing lift to the spirits it gives at spring's beginning, boldly presenting its marvellous flowers in what seem to be very inauspicious conditions. The tree reaches 5 m (15 feet) ultimately and the flowers are very large – 15 cm (6 inches) across when open. White, pink and purple-flowering varieties are in cultivation. Give this species shelter from biting winds.

Prunus If you have space for only one flowering tree it would be difficult to better one of the ornamental *Prunus*. All varieties furnish long sprays bearing pink or white flowers. Choose from: Flowering Almond (*P. dulcis*), height and spread 6–8 m (18–25 feet), with clusters of pink flowers; *P. avium* 'Plena', height and spread about 10 m (30 feet) with pendent clusters of numerous white flowers; *P. serrula,* height 6 m (20 feet), spread 4.5 m (15 feet), for its glossy red-brown bark; *P.* 'Kiku-shidare Sakura' (Japanese Cherry), whose branches and branchlets curve downwards. The young leaves are bronze-green, the double flowers deep pink. Shrubby species include *P. glandulosa*, 1.5 × 1.5 m (5 × 5 feet) and *P. tenella*, 90 × 90 cm (3 × 3 feet). The variety 'Fire Hill' has deep pink flowers.

Rhododendrons and Azaleas This large group of showy spreading shrubs flourish best in sheltered woodland. They will not grow on limy soil. Hardy evergreen hybrids reach about 3–5 m (10–15 feet), possibly more. The trumpet-shaped blooms and large leathery leaves are magnificent. 'Christmas Cheer' is an early flowerer with blush-pink blooms. Late in May the choice widens enormously. Notable are: 'Dawn's Delight,' deep carmine in the bud, soft pink when open; 'Goldsworth Orange', pale orange and 'Goldsworth Yellow', apricot fading to pale yellow (these two are smaller than the average – about 1.5 × 1.5 m (5 × 5 feet)); 'Mrs A. T. de la Mare', white with a green throat; 'Purple Splendour', deep purple with darker streaks, and 'Susan' for its fine foliage and lilac flowers.

Spiraea *Spiraea* x *arguta* is the form known as Bridal Wreath, and indeed its long arching sprays of graceful white flowers are perfect for wedding decorations. Growing to 1.8 × 1.8 m (6 × 6 feet), it is useful as a flowering hedge. For this purpose, plant shrubs 38–60 cm (15–24 inches) apart and prune to 15 cm (6 inches) high. Tip prune the first year's growth when 7.5 cm (3 inches) long. Clip annually after flowering.

Viburnum *Viburnum* x *burkwoodii*. This spring-flowering species is an evergreen and may reach 2.4 m (8 feet) with a spread of 2.7–3.6 m (9–12 feet). The white flowers are sweetly scented, carried in flat 7.5-cm (3-inch) wide heads. Plant in autumn or spring in a spot that enjoys full sun and some shelter from harsh winds. A moist, fertile soil is best.

Willow *Salix* spp. Willows are useful in new gardens because they grow quickly, as well as being particularly graceful. Other characteristics endear them to the flower arranger, such as the yellow catkins of spring (all species), the vivid red stems of autumn (*S. daphnoides*), and the gentle green of the summer foliage. *S. aegyptiaca* is the best choice for small gardens at a mature height of 4 m (12 feet). Moist soil is an essential requirement, and a sunny position is best. Plant between late autumn and early spring.

The Summer Garden

BULBS

Dahlia The border Dahlias have been divided into several complex groups, and the enthusiast should visit a specialist nursery or Dahlia exhibition before making a choice. Though they are best given a bed to themselves, one or two plants could be tried out in the mixed border where the spectacular and vividly coloured blooms make a great impact. Look out for cactus flowered, ball, decorative and pompon varieties, in a delectable range of hues of orange, yellow, russet, red, pink, lilac and white. Plant unsprouted tubers in mid-April, sprouted tubers in May. A well-drained soil is essential. The site should be prepared by digging in peat, well-rotted manure or garden compost in autumn. Before planting, work in a top-dressing of 100 g/m² (4 oz per sq. yard) of bone meal. Staking is necessary.

Gladiolus Ideally, Gladioli that are intended for cutting should be grown in rows in a special bed; in the mixed border they look best in small random groups, but the overall balance of the border may be upset if they are gathered for decoration. It is worth attempting to solve this dilemma because the colour range extends far beyond even the most eclectic florists' offering. The species, such as *G. tristis*, have a delicacy far removed from the triumphant large-flowered hybrids. *G. tristis* is only 45 cm (18 inches) high, its scented parchment-coloured flowers loosely arranged along the stem. A choice from the large-flowered hybrids might include 'Aristocrat', deep rich red; 'Forgotten Dreams', primrose tinged deep red, and 'Green Woodpecker', green. All these may reach 1.2 m (4 feet); of the miniatures, reaching 45 cm–1 m (18 inches–3 feet) and with smaller florets, 'Greenbird', acid-yellow, is very floriferous and 'Zenith' particularly pretty with ruffled pink petals.

Lily *Lilium* spp. Like the rose, the lily is apt to induce such passionate devotion that the gardener who starts with one or two risks giving up all his space and attention to them within a few seasons. The one to start with might well be *L. regale*, height 1.2–1.8 m (4–6 feet), hardy, and quick to increase. The spectacular white blooms are fragrant and carried in loose clusters. Excellent for church decoration. The pale mauve blooms of *L. mackliniae* are more fragile in appearance, though it too is perfectly hardy. A stunning yellow lily is 'Limelight', a vigorous hybrid. Lilies need protection from strong winds. Well-drained soil enriched with leaf-mould, well-rotted compost or peat and with good drainage is required.

ANNUALS AND BIENNIALS

African Marigold *Tagetes erecta* differs from the common Pot Marigold in that its blooms are more like pompoms and the colour range is basically yellow. Soil requirements are for a well-drained, medium loam. Sow seeds under glass in March/April and plant out in a sunny site in May. For tall plants 'Yellow Climax', 75 cm (2 feet 6 inches), is recommended; 'First Lady' is only 38 cm (15 inches) tall and bears abundant primrose-yellow flowers.

Aster *Callistephus chinensis*. In appearance resembling both a Daisy and a Chrysanthemum, Asters have been developed in several distinctive strains of which three are of particular interest to arrangers. The Ball type are 75 cm

(2 feet 6 inches) tall, erect, with incurved double flowers, Lilliputs reach 38 cm (15 inches) and form a dense dome of round blooms. Queen of the Market Asters are the same height but bear large, double flowers. The colour range is red, pink, purple and white. Because Asters are subject to callistephus wilt they should not be grown in the same ground for two consecutive years. They may be raised from seed down under glass in March, the seedlings gradually being hardened off until planting out in May, or sown directly into the flowering site in April. Any well-drained soil will do, but a sunny site is best.

Clarkia *Clarkia elegans* is a tall-growing (up to 60 cm (24 inches)) and deservedly popular garden plant. Sow seeds in March where they are to flower, in light loam in a sunny site. From July to September long spikes of colourful double flowers appear. The mixed varieties generally available include white, lavender, apricot and scarlet.

Clary *Salvia horminum*. This attractive plant, height 45 cm (1 foot 6 inches), is always popular. Pink, blue or white bracts surround the spikes of insignificant white flowers and make Clary a useful addition to the decorative border. It is very robust and requires no staking. Sow the seeds in April, where the plants are to flower.

Cornflower *Centaurea cyanus*. The familiar wild Cornflower has been improved by plant breeders to produce a tall (60 cm–1 m (2–3 feet)), robust plant with large flowers not only of the well-known bright blue ('Blue Diadem') but also, in the mixed strains, pink, lavender and white. Sow seed in the flowering site in April. A fertile soil and sunny site is best, and staking may be necessary.

French Marigold *Tagetes patula*. Compact plants, about 23 cm (9 inches) high. French Marigolds need the same treatment as the African ones. Their colours are particularly rich and vibrant, from clear yellow to rich russet, and can look marvellous with copper, brass or pewter containers if the touch is light. 'Monarch Mixed' is a good variety.

Godetia *Godetia grandiflora*. Similar to Clarkia, to which they are related, Godetias are more bushy in habit, furnishing medium-length stems. The colour choice ranges from red, pink and white to apricot, and the petals of the variety 'Azalea-flowered' are frilled and curving. To encourage abundant flowering the soil should not be over-rich, but moist and in a sunny site. Seed may be sown outside the previous autumn or in March/April.

Helichrysum *Helichrysum bracteatum*. Commonly called Everlasting Flowers, Helichrysums are a basic constituent of many dried arrangements. The daisy-like flowers, 5 cm (2 inches) across, may be white, yellow, orange, red or pink. Double and dwarf forms are available; the species reaches 1 m (3 feet) and its bushy habit makes it useful as a border plant. 'Hot Bikini' reaches only 30 cm (1 foot). Sow seeds under glass in March and plant out hardened-off seedlings in May in light, well-drained soil on a sunny site.

Larkspur *Delphinium consolida*. These are the Stock-flowered and Imperial Larkspurs, reaching 1–1.5 m (3–5 feet) and carrying spires of blue, white, pink, purple or red flowers above attractive fern-like foliage. The spires are also useful in arrangements when they are still in bud, especially the pink-flowered varieties. They like deep, rich soil and full sun. Sow seed outside in autumn and give protection during the winter. Staking may not be necessary if the site is sheltered from strong winds.

Love-in-a-mist *Nigella damascena* is easy to grow – sow seeds in March where it is to flower – and seeds itself freely. The popular variety 'Miss Jekyll' is a typical bright blue with feathery foliage, the flowers wreathed with gossamer-like bracts. In autumn, the seed-pods are equally decorative globes of pale brown. 'Persian Jewels Mixed' is a strain with mauve, purple, pink and white blooms in addition to blue. Height 60 cm (24 inches) but no staking necessary.

Phlox *Phlox drummondii* thrives in any fertile soil where drainage is good. Closely packed flowers are carried on erect stems, 38 cm (15 inches) long, slightly shorter in the larger flowered Grandiflora group. The colour range complements Clarkia admirably: cream, deep pink, deep red and purple.

Pot Marigold *Calendula officinalis* owes its name to its use in cooking. They will grow almost anywhere, but prefer a well-drained medium soil. Sow in autumn and give protection over the winter. It is important to pinch out the growing tips to encourage plenty of side shoots for cutting. Although growing to 60 cm (24 inches) supports are unnecessary as the plants are very sturdy. The bright orange many-petalled flowers can be up to 10 cm (4 inches) across. 'Orange King' is a strong clear orange; 'Pacific Beauty' mixtures include apricot and cream. 'Fiesta Gitana' is a mixture growing only 30 cm (1 foot) high.

Scabious *Scabiosa atropurpurea*. These tall plants (1 m/ 3 feet) may need staking but otherwise are easy to raise on fertile, well-drained soil. The pliable, graceful stems bear Dahlia-like flowers of purple, blue, pink, apricot and white. The seed-heads are useful for dried arrangements. Because of its sombre dignity the deep purple variety used often to be included in funeral wreaths.

A riot of colour in a summer garden, dominated by the rich blue of Delphiniums.

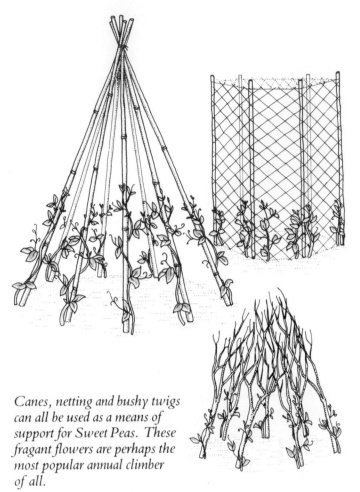

Canes, netting and bushy twigs can all be used as a means of support for Sweet Peas. These fragrant flowers are perhaps the most popular annual climber of all.

Sweet Pea *Lathyrus odoratus* repays many times over the little extra attention it requires for finest results. Double-dig the plot the previous autumn, incorporating well-rotted manure at the bottom of the trench. Sow seeds in pots in September and plant out the seedlings when hardened off in April. March-sown seedlings may be planted out in May. When the young plants are 10 cm (4 inches) high, pinch out the growing point to encourage the development of side shoots. Sweet Peas may reach 3 m (10 feet) in good conditions, so some method of support is essential, whether canes, netting, or bushy twigs. The delicate winged petals are carried on fragile green stems wound with tendrils. In the Spencer group the broad colour range includes 'Leamington', deep lilac; 'Margot', cream; 'Nancy', cream-pink; 'Tribute', cherry red; 'Jupiter', maroon, and 'Piccadilly', apricot. Dwarf varieties are also available in the groups Bijou, 45 cm (18 inches), Knee-hi, 60 cm–1.2 m (2–4 feet) and Colour Carpet, 20 cm (8 inches), though the last is of least use to the arranger. All kinds are sweet-smelling.

Sweet Sultan *Centaurea moschata* bears a close resemblance to its relative the Cornflower, but because the petals are less tightly packed they are more versatile plants for decorative schemes, where they can be used to introduce an element of white, pink or purple. The yellow-flowering kind has smaller heads. Sow seed in April in the flowering site in a sunny position. Height 60 cm (24 inches).

ORNAMENTAL GRASSES TO GROW FROM SEED

Name	Height	Inflorescence
Agrostis nebulosa (Cloud Grass)	38 cm (15 in)	Numerous tiny panicles
Briza maxima (Pearl Grass)	30–50 cm (12–20 in)	Nodding panicles suitable for Christmas when glittered
Briza gracilis syn. B. minor (Little Quaking Grass)	23–30 cm (9–12 in)	Shakes in the breeze
Coix lacryma-jobi (Job's Tears)	45–60 cm (18–24 in)	Grey-green seed pods
Eragrostis elegans syn. E. interrupta (Love Grass)	30–60 cm (12–24 in)	Long, graceful many-flowered panicles
Gymnothrix latifolia syn. Pennisetum latifolium	1–1.2 m (3–4 ft)	Large nodding spikes
Hordeum jubatum (Squirrel Tail Grass)	23–30 cm (9–12 in)	Tufts like a long furry tail
Lagurus ovatus (Hare's Tail Grass)	30 cm (12 in)	Stubby tufts
Miscanthus sinensis syn. Eulalia japonica	1–1.5 m (3–5 ft)	Foliage only – narrow, blue-green leaves
M.s. 'Zebrinus'	1–1.2 m (3–4 ft)	Leaves striped horizontally with yellow
Pennisetum villosum syn. P. longistylum	45–60 cm (18–24 in)	Delicate white or purple plumes
P. ruppelii syn. P. setaceum (Fountain Grass)	60 cm–1 m (2–3 ft)	Abundant cream spikes tinged green or purple
Stipa pennata (Feather Grass)	75 cm (2 ft 6 in)	Silvery plumes
Zea mays (Ornamental Sweet Corn) var. 'Quadricolor'	1–1.5 m (3–5 ft)	Small cobs; leaves variegated white, pale yellow and rose
var. 'Japonica'		Leaves striped white

PERENNIALS

African Lily *Agapanthus* spp. Despite their exotic nationality, these plants are hardy enough to grow outside in warmer parts of the country. They bear spherical heads of blue blooms on a tall – up to 1 m (3 feet) – stem, above a clump of strap-like leaves. *A. praecox* is evergreen and a white variety is in cultivation. Headbourne Hybrids have been developed from the species to give greater hardiness with a wider colour range, from very pale blue to intense purple. Plant outdoors in April. Choose a site that will offer shelter from the winds but not shade. They like sun and a fertile soil with adequate drainage, but dislike disturbance once established. The seed-heads are a stately addition to dried arrangements, but if not needed for this purpose the stems should be cut down after flowering.

Alstroemeria *Alstroemeria aurantiaca*. Sometimes known as the Peruvian Lily, this hardy species bears a cluster of scarlet lily-like blooms on erect 1 m (3 ft) stems. Set out plants carefully in early spring in well-drained fertile soil. They may take a year to become established, and will not take kindly to being moved in maturity – so make sure you put them where you really want them to stay. They look superb in the border, vivid but graceful. 'Dover Orange' is a good choice, and 'Lutea', bright yellow with pinky-red streaks, is recommended.

Anaphalis *Anaphalis yedoensis* is a bushy plant with much to recommend it: the pure white of its spreading, everlasting flower-heads, the abundant grey-green foliage and ease of cultivation. Useful in both fresh and dried arrangements, it will tolerate sun or shade but needs sharp drainage. Set out plants any time from September to March.

Anemone *Anemone* x *hybrida*. Summer- and autumn-flowering anemones are more delicately coloured than their spring sisters, the pink or white flowers more open and daisy-like. The stems reach up to 1.2 m (4 ft), generally 60 cm–1 m (2–3 ft) 'Louise Uhink' is a good white variety, 'Queen Charlotte' a double-flowered pink. Like many other perennials they take a season or two to get established, and resent subsequent disturbance. Give them a partially shaded site, with moisture-retentive soil, and plant between October and March.

Astilbe The elegant feathery plumes formed by the minuscule flowers of Astilbes are set off by deeply cut leaves that are reddish when young. Varieties of *A.* x *arendsii* 60 cm–1 m (2–3 ft) are available in many shades of pink, red and white. They are equally happy in sun or shade as long as the soil is kept moist. Plant at any time from October to March. Lift and divide the plants to prevent overcrowding every 3 or 4 years.

Anthemis *Anthemis tinctoria*. Known as Ox-eye Chamomile, this species is a taller relative of the Common Chamomile sometimes used for lawns. Wide daisy-like flowers of cream or yellow are borne on 75 cm (2 feet 6 inches) stems with prettily cut leaves. Plant any time from October to March. Any fertile soil will do but they like sun and will need some support if exposed to winds. After the flowering season, cut the stems down.

Bergamot *Monarda didyma*. Like Clary, Bergamot belongs in the herb garden. Its leaves, when dried, are used to make a soothing tea, but its brilliantly coloured flower-heads, like ruffled daisies, make it welcome in the decorative border and in floral arrangements. The best-known variety is red, 'Cambridge Scarlet', but other good varieties are 'Croftway Pink', 'Melissa', pale pink, 'Snow Maiden', white, and 'Blue Stocking', purple. Plant in autumn or spring in moist soil in partial shade and do not let the soil dry out.

Campanula Among the charming perennial relatives of the familiar biennial Canterbury Bell, *C. medium*, are some of the loveliest garden plants in the colour ranges blue and white. Those with bell-shaped flowers include *C. alliariifolia*, 45–60 cm (18–24 inches), with grey-green heart-shaped leaves and spires of white flowers; *C.*

glomerata 'Dahurica', 45–60 cm (18–24 inches), which bears a cluster of purple heads at the top of the stem and *C. lactiflora*, 1–1.5 m (3–5 feet), with branching stems of light lilac flowers and bushy foliage. *C. persicifolia*, 30 cm–1 m (1–3 feet), is a narrow-leaved evergreen with white or blue star-shaped flowers and is a perfect outline material for an arrangement. The flowers of *C. carpatica* are also star-shaped but the stems shorter – 23–30 cm (9–12 inches). The variety 'Turbinata' has grey, hairy foliage. Campanulas like well-drained fertile soil and will tolerate sun or partial shade. Taller varieties need staking.

Campion *Lychnis* spp. Campions bear their flowers in groups of varying density, some rather like Primulas –

L. flos-jovis is an example – others much smaller and tightly packed, as in *L. chalcedonica*. Each individual flower is open-faced and in the red colour range from scarlet and orange to magenta and shocking pink. The leaves are sometimes silvery and in the case of *L. coronaria*, woolly. The average height is 60 cm (24 inches) and staking may be necessary in exposed places. Plant from October to March in well-drained soil on a sunny or partially shaded site.

Columbine *Aquilegia vulgaris* is one of that group of plants redolent of English cottage gardens, and like Love-in-a-mist it produces many seeds. The flowers are tubular with spurs that in the hybrids are markedly long. Coloured pink, cream, yellow, violet, magenta and white, Columbines reach 1 m (3 feet) but do not need supports. The pale green leaves look very like Maidenhair Fern. Plant out Columbines in September in moist but well-drained soil. They will tolerate some shade. Cut down the stems after flowering.

Creeping Jenny *Lysimachia nummularia*. This evergreen species is also known as Moneywort, because its flowers look like gold coins lying on the ground. Excellent for ground cover anywhere but especially near water, and as a trailing element in arrangements. Plant from autumn to spring.

Delphinium *Delphinium elatum*. There can be few flower arrangers who, if asked to name their top ten plants, would omit Delphiniums; yet in the garden they need tactful treatment if their neighbours in the border are not to be totally overshadowed. The heavenly blue can look too intense against anything other than green.

Since their height may be 1.2 m (6 feet) they are likely to be at the back of the border. If an old mellow wall or tall hedge is behind, well and good, but an undistinguished fence might best be disguised by a Clematis (a vigorous evergreen like *C. armandii* on a large expanse), a climbing rose ('May Queen') or honeysuckle. Large flowered and Belladonna varieties are available, and in both the colour range extends beyond the blue of the species. The Belladonnas are generally shorter and their spires of open-faced flowers less densely carried. It is worth attending a Delphinium show to make a choice, but worth considering are 'Blue Jade', 'Silver Moon', and 'Purple Ruffles'; of the Belladonnas, 'Bonita', gentian blue, 'Wendy', deep blue flecked with purple, and 'Pink Sensation'. Plant Delphiniums from September to March in deep rich soil, or sow seed in early spring in the flowering site. They like a sunny position, with some shelter from the winds, and will need firm staking.

Echinops *Echinops humilis* (Globe Thistle). Useful mainly when dried for everlasting arrangements, the dreamy blue of the Globe Thistle makes it an attractive and unusual

OPPOSITE: *A display of low-growing summer annuals.*
ABOVE: *A colourful herbaceous border, including* Achillea
filipendulina *'Gold Plate',* Pyrethrum roseum *and*
Papaver orientale *'Marcus Perry'.*

garden plant. They like a sunny position but are not fussy
about soil type. If not gathered for arrangement, the stems
should be cut down in autumn. Plant in October. Height
about 1.2 m (4 feet).

Eryngium Grown together with Echinops, the Eryn-
giums make an interesting variation on the theme of
silvery blue: their flower-heads are surrounded by rays of
pointed metallic-looking bracts and all varieties have
deeply cut delicate leaves. Good in dried decorations and a
challenge to the designer. *E. alpinum*, 45–60 cm
(18–24 inches), *E.* x *oliverianum*, 1–1.2 m (3–4 feet), and
E. planum, 60 cm (24 inches) are good choices. In *E.
maritimum* – Sea Holly – the bracts are coloured green and
very like common Holly leaves in shape. Any soil will
suffice, though a sunny site is to be preferred. Plant
between October and April.

Filipendula *Filipendula hexapetala*. The variety 'Flora
Pleno' is a hardy herbaceous plant reaching 45–60 cm (18–

24 inches) and bearing large fluffy heads of little white
star-like flowers. The leaves are fern-like. This would
make an interesting addition to wedding decorations. It
needs full sun and good drainage.

Foxglove *Digitalis purpurea* is an undemanding and showy
plant. Tall spikes of bell-like flowers in white, pink or
purple rise above a flat rosette of wide mid-green leaves.
They like partial shade and will reach 1.2 m (4 feet) without staking. They are suitable for placing at the back of the
border and for tall arrangements when cut. They are
normally biennial.

Gaillardia *Gaillardia aristata*. The hybrids of this species
provide colourful variation on the form of the open-faced
Daisy. 'Burgundy' is deep red; 'Mandarin' deep orange
and yellow. At 75 cm (2 feet 6 inches) twiggy supports
are required. Plant in spring in light soil in a sunny site,
though if space is short they will tolerate some shade.

Geum *Geum chiloense*. The cup-shaped flowers of Geum
are so vivid, the stems so delicate, they sometimes look
like splashes of velvet suspended in space. 'Mrs Bradshaw'
is a bright scarlet, 'Lady Stratheden' rich yellow. 'Prince of
Orange' is another good choice. Plant in autumn in any
soil; peat or well-rotted leaf mould previously worked in

is an advantage. A sunny or shaded site will serve. At 60 cm (24 inches), twiggy supports may be necessary.

Golden Rod *Solidago* x *hybrida*. The old varieties of this vivid yellow perennial were tall, but now many dwarf kinds are available, some only 30 cm (1 foot). The right variety carefully positioned (they are happy in half-shade) can bring an appropriate glow of colour to the late summer border. 'Goldenmosa' reaches a manageable 1 m (3 feet) and bears outward-stretching sprays of tiny flowers. The narrow pointed leaves are a compatible greeny-yellow; the 1.2–1.5 m (4–5 feet) 'Mimosa' bears its flowers in arching golden plumes. Sixty-cm (2-foot) stakes are needed. Plant from October to March in any soil. Cut the stems down after flowering in Autumn.

Gypsophila *Gypsophila paniculata*. The drift of tiny white or pale pink blossoms is as effective in the border as in arrangements. Gypsophilas dislike disturbance, so decide carefully on their position before planting. The site should be sunny, the soil well-drained and not too acid: dress lightly with lime before planting if necessary. Plant in October.

Heuchera *Heuchera sanguinea*. This member of the Saxifrage family bears panicles of diminutive red flowers on very fine 45 cm (18 inch) stems, giving a feathery effect that softens over-formal arrangements. They look particularly pretty grouped with roses. Different hues are found in 'Pretty Polly', rose pink, 'Sunset', scarlet, and 'Bressingham Blaze', coral. 'Pearl Drops' is a white form well worth cultivating. A light, well-drained soil is essential. The site may be in sun or partial shade. Plant between October and April.

Hosta Almost all gardens can benefit from a planting of Hostas; certainly, few flower arrangers would like to be without these broad-leaved handsome plants. In shade and a moisture-retentive soil, they provide inimitably luxurious ground cover. Though less showy than the leaves, the slender stems of drooping flowers are attractive too, in white, pink or lavender. Many varieties have variegated leaves. Plant from autumn to spring.

Lady's Mantle *Alchemilla mollis*. This tall, hardy, herbaceous plant is a very useful member of the flower arranger's border. Its broad shapely leaves form a rosette at the base and, singly, embrace the stem as it rises to a cloud of tiny pale green-yellow flowers at the top. It will self-seed freely (too freely for some) and grow in almost any conditions. Height 30–45 cm (12–18 inches) but staking may be necessary.

Limonium *Limonium latifolium*. Raised mainly for value in dried arrangements, Limoniums make an attractive garden feature, reaching 60 cm (24 inches) and forming an open dome of lavender panicles. 'Blue Cloud' is a good

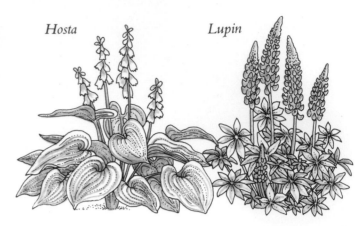

Hosta   *Lupin*

and aptly named variety. Plant in early spring in well-drained soil on a sunny site.

Lupin *Lupinus polyphyllus*. The perennial Lupins in general cultivation are hybrids known as Russell Lupins. They carry their numerous flowers in tall spires above attractive mid-green foliage, each leaf divided up like an open hand but with about a dozen slender fingers. As each flower may be of two colours, Lupins are versatile for the arranger and in certain combinations bring a soft, cottage-garden feeling to the border. 'Elsie Waters', in two shades of pink, is a good example; 'Jane Eyre', violet and white is another. More striking are 'Josephine', grey-blue and sharp yellow; 'Limelight', bright yellow, and 'Guardsman', orange.

Mullein *Verbascum* spp. This is a real flower arranger's favourite. Tall and dignified, its bowl-shaped flowers are mostly in various shades of yellow, but white and rose-pink varieties are available. The basal rosette of leaves is an attractive feature. The group of hybrids to which the best varieties belong reach from 60 cm (24 inches) to 2 m (6 feet). All bear long spikes of flowers. They like a light soil and full sun. Plant in autumn or spring and cut the plants right down after flowering.

Nicotiana *Nicotiana affinis*. Usually grown as an annual, these tall – 60 cm–1 m (2–3 feet) – fragrant plants bear numerous slightly drooping tubular flowers. Mixed varieties are available which include red, pink, cream and magenta in the colour range. 'Lime Green' is an aptly named variety especially attractive to the flower arranger. Sow seeds under glass in February and harden seedlings off gradually before planting out in May. A sunny site on rich soil with good drainage is best. Staking may be necessary if no protection from winds is offered.

Oenothera *Oenothera missouriensis* is a low-growing (15 cm/ 6 inches) subject useful for the front of the border. The large, fragile-looking pale yellow flowers, which open in the evening, look superb against the narrow dark green leaves. As the main stem lies on the ground, this species is good for trailing elements. Plant in well-drained

Pink   *Rudbeckia*

soil any time from October to March in sun or light shade.

Paeony *Paeonia* spp. With their splendid spherical flowers in red, pink, white or yellow and strong dark green stems with handsome foliage, clumps of Paeonies are a must for the herbaceous border and furnish excellent cut flowers. *P. lactiflora* hybrids, 1m (3 feet), include, among the singles, 'Augustus John', deep cerise, and 'Globe of Light', pale pink. Good double-flowered varieties are 'Madame Calot', pink turning white, and 'Karl Rosenfeld', burgundy. Paeonies are not the easiest plants to cultivate and once established should not be disturbed. Prepare the plot by digging in well-rotted manure to a depth of at least one spit. Set the crowns between September and March 2.5 cm (1 inch) deep. Give the plants an annual mulch in spring and do not let them thirst in dry weather. Cut down foliage after flowering.

Physostegia *Physostegia virginiana*. Because the individual flowers on the spikes of this species will remain in whatever position they are put, this has been dubbed the 'Obedient Plant'. Tubular with a frilled edge, the flowers may be pink, lilac or white. They are closely packed on the stem, and since they do not open all at once, but randomly, green is an important element. Plants may reach 1.2 m (4 feet) if the soil is rich; they like moisture and will thrive in sun or half-shade. Plant in autumn or spring.

Pink *Dianthus* spp. Together with the Sweet Pea, Pinks embody the spirit of early summer, fragrant, fragile and joyful. It pays to prepare the site well, as the plants will be there for many seasons. Dig one spit deep and work in some well-rotted manure. The soil should not be too rich, and drainage must be good. A sunny open position is best. Raising from seed, sown in April/May, is easy and hardened off plants may be set out in June/July.

The two main groups are old-fashioned Pinks, hybrids of the variety *D. plumarius*, and modern Pinks, the hybrid *D.* x *allwoodii*. Both grow to 25–38 cm (10–15 inches). Of the old-fashioned type 'Mrs Sinkins', white, is a great favourite; 'Inchmery', pale pink, and 'Dad's Favourite', white, each petal laced purple, are also recommended, but

all only flower once, in June. Modern Pinks produce many more flowers and go on throughout the summer. There are many to choose from, of which the following stand out: 'Doris', salmon pink with a pale crimson centre; 'London Glow', very dark velvety red, finely edged with pink; 'Robina', bright scarlet; 'Timothy', silvery pink flecked with deeper pink.

Pyrethrum These are technically classified as Chrysanthemums. Pyrethrums bear daisy-like flowers with wide yellow centres in white, and hues of red or pink. They make an appealing addition to a sunny border. Several varieties grown – and picked – together look even better. 'Eileen May Robinson' is a good clear pink, 'Kelway's Glorious' bright red. At 1 m (3 feet), the support of canes is needed. Plant in spring on light well-drained soil.

Rudbeckia (Black-eyed Susan). There are perennial forms of this plant that are undemanding and colourful additions to the border. The blooms, which are often present from late summer into October, are usually yellow with a raised brown centre. Height varies from about 60 cm– 1 m (2–3 feet), and there are several kinds. *R. deamii* is particularly free flowering and grows to about 90 cm (almost 3 feet). One of the dwarfest, and with a really black eye, is *R. newmannii*; the petals are warm yellow and it reaches about 60 cm (2 feet). Different in appearance is the double-flowered 'Goldquelle', which forms a bushy plant of about 75 cm (2½ feet). Choose an open, sunny site on fertile, well-drained soil.

Shasta Daisy *Chrysanthemum maximum*. Chrysanthemums can be very demanding plants to grow, but this species is hardy and floriferous. With very little attention it furnishes tall – 75 cm–1 m (2½–3 feet) – stems with wide white daisy heads with yellow centres. 'Wirral Pride' is a double form at the taller end of the range. A little lime in a fertile soil will suit Shasta Daisies, which should be planted in September or April. Lift the plants, divide and replant them every third spring. Keep a sharp eye out for pests – eelworms and earwigs are a particular problem.

Sidalcea. These are among the most trouble-free hardy border plants. They form compact plants, and even though some may reach 1 m (3 feet) they do not require staking. The spikes of small, hollyhock-like flowers are carried well clear of the foliage, and most will be in bloom for several months, usually in July and August. 'Rose Queen' is one of the most popular varieties, having graceful spikes of rose-pink flowers. One of the most compact forms is 'Loveliness', a shell-pink that grows to about 75 cm (2½ feet). 'Croftway Red' is a good deep red. The plants will grow well in ordinary soil in a sunny position. They can be divided and replanted with benefit every three years.

Thalictrum Though these are most often cultivated for their exquisitely delicate foliage, Thalictrums are in all their parts most attractive plants. The panicles of tiny flowers have a light gossamer effect which well balances out arrangements with globe-shaped flowers like Paeonies or old Roses. The three best are *T. adiantifolium*, leaves like Maidenhair Fern, 1 m (3 feet), minute purple flowers; *T. aquilegifolium*, leaves like Columbine, 60 cm–1 m (2–3 feet), rose-pink conspicuous flower-heads, and *T. dipterocarpum*, 1.2–1.5 m (4–5 feet), flowers like a tall-growing London Pride. Plant in spring in rich soil in sun or partial shade. Staking is required. Cut down the stems in autumn.

Trollius *Trollius* x *hybridus*. This, the Globe Flower, well merits a place in the flower arranger's garden. Its beautifully rounded shape alone recommends it, as do its deeply cut dark green leaves. All varieties are yellow: 'Canary Bird' is the palest, 'Goldquelle' the deepest. Moist soil is essential and it should not be allowed to dry out. Plant in autumn or spring in sun or light shade.

TREES AND SHRUBS

Ceanothus When viewed at close quarters the panicles of these wall shrubs resemble lilac blooms. They are blue or violet, and are borne in June in great profusion. *C. thyrsiflorus* is a particular beauty, a sturdy evergreen which may be grown as a small tree. Plant in late summer/early autumn or late spring in good light soil. It is not advisable to grow Ceanothus on soil with a high lime content.

Clematis It is the small-flowered species *Clematis montana* whose varieties are so often seen embracing a door or porch, and whose stems add flow and flourish to trailing arrangements. *C. m. wilsonii* is a summer flowerer with white blooms. Amongst the hybrids the colour choice is broad. Recommended are 'Ernest Markham', vivid scarlet; 'Beauty of Worcester', purple with cream stamens, and 'Henryi', white. *C. tangutica* needs generous space, but rewards with yellow flowers and silvery seed-heads. The small white star-shaped flowers of *C. flammula* are fragrant, those of *C. orientalis* yellow and pendent. Plant Clematis from autumn to spring in a spot where their roots and main stem base will be shaded from strong sun. A slightly alkaline soil is best.

Deutzia A particularly good choice where space is limited is *D.* x *elegantissima* 1.2 × 1.2 m (4 × 4 feet), with its upright form. In June it bears panicles of pink flowers on arching stems with pointed leaves. Plant from October to February in any well-drained soil. The site should not be too exposed to wind and weather.

Escallonia There are several very pleasant hybrid forms of this evergreen flowering shrub which are useful for hedging. The leaves are oval and glossy, the blooms freely borne. 'Apple Blossom' is aptly named; 'C.F. Ball' is the hardiest and bears red flowers. Escallonia is lovely to use for side sprays in large flower decorations. Plant in autumn or spring.

Eucryphia *Eucryphia glutinosa*. Chosen for its hardiness, this species is upright in habit rather like a Christmas tree – but it is decked out in high summer, with a profusion of white flowers with prominent yellow stamens. The glossy green leaves turn orange in autumn. Height 3 m (10 feet), spread 2–2.4 m (6–8 feet). Plant in early autumn on slightly acid soil – this species will not tolerate lime – in a sheltered, sunny spot.

Gleditschia *Gleditschia triacanthos* (Honey Locust). These tall (6–10 m/18–30 feet) handsome, deciduous trees have delicately pretty leaves of pale green, divided into as many as 32 slender leaflets. The variety 'Sunburst' bears yellow leaves in spring. Any well-drained soil is acceptable. Plant from October to March in full sun.

Honeysuckle *Lonicera* spp. Of the many species of this climber in cultivation two may be singled out for the arranger: *L. periclymenum* 'Serotina', with flowers glowing red outside, buttery yellow within, and *L. tragophylla*, with vivid golden-yellow flowers. Both reach about 6 m (20 feet). They like light shade and humus-rich soil with good drainage. Plant in spring.

Laburnum These delightful and eye-catching trees are sometimes grown in close avenues, where their myriad drooping yellow flowers make a sunlit tunnel. A single specimen, however, is as delightful to gaze on. In small gardens *L. anagyroides* 'Pendulum', height 3 m (10 feet), is best. Unfortunately, Laburnums are susceptible to honey fungus, a disease which first shows itself when the flowers fail to open. Speedy removal of affected parts is essential. Plant young trees any time from October to March. All parts of the plant are poisonous. Take care in gardens where children play to remove fallen seed-pods from the ground.

Mock Orange *Philadelphus* spp. It is the delicious fragrance, closely resembling that of orange blossom, which gives Philadelphus its popular name. As recommended hybrids vary in size, most gardens should have room for a specimen. At the smaller end of the range is 'Avalanche', about 1.5 × 1.5 m (5 × 5 feet); 'Virginal', 2.4 × 2.4 m (8 × 8 feet), has double flowers; one of the tallest is 'Burfordensis', 3 × 3.6 m (10 × 12 feet). All have white flowers. This deciduous shrub is easy to grow in any well-drained

Climbing roses in full bloom cover the front of a country cottage.

128

soil, in sun or partial shade. Plant from October to April.

Robinia *Robinia pseudoacacia*. Justly popular as specimen trees, Robinias (False Acacias) are tolerant of polluted town air. They may reach 10 m (30 feet), and the spread of their branches may be 3–5 m (10–15 feet). The light green, oval leaves always look sun-dappled and mobile. In June, racemes of cream-coloured flowers very like Laburnum appear. The leaves of the variety 'Frisia' are a rich golden-yellow from spring to autumn. A bright, sunny spot is best, with some protection from wind. Any well-drained soil will do. Plant from October to April.

Rose *Rosa* spp. Since the number of rose varieties is beyond counting, any selection is bound to be highly controversial. Visits to specialist growers and rose shows are a pleasant duty when making a choice. The old roses are amongst the loveliest, and it would help to keep them in cultivation if gardeners less susceptible to the showy charms of modern varieties could find space for one or two like 'Boule de Neige', white, Bourbon; 'Cardinal Richelieu', dark purple, Gallica, or 'Baroness Rothschild', pink, Hybrid perpetual. Species roses with decorative hips are *R. pomifera* (pale pink flowers), *R. rugosa* (deep pink flowers; hybrids of several other colours have been developed) and *R. moyesii* (red flowers). Hybrid Teas are popular because they have a long flowering season and last well when cut. The colour range is extremely broad. Some particularly suitable for flower arrangements are:

  'Blessings', coral pink
  'Blue Moon', silvery-lilac
  'Julia's Rose', parchment brown
  'Margaret Merrill', pale creamy-pink
  'Iceberg', pure white
  'National Trust', red
  'Spek's Yellow', bright, rich yellow

Modern shrub roses are good at the back of the border; 'Constance Spry', pink with bowl-shaped blooms, is a deservedly popular choice amongst arrangers. Climbing roses are excellent for walls, pillars and pergolas: to clothe an unsightly feature fast, choose 'Wedding Day'; for a mass of heavy, full, pink blooms.

Experts differ on how and when to prune roses. What is more certain is that, for all their beauty, they are accommodating plants that will thrive on most soils as long as they are given enough to drink and protected against pests (notably aphids) and diseases (especially black spot and mildew).

The Autumn Garden

BULBS

Autumn Crocus *Colchicum* spp. These low-growing 15 cm (6 inch) plants are best in places where their over-abundant foliage, which survives the flowers, will not be obtrusive. Of the various species, *C. speciosum* has the greatest colour choice in the pink/crimson/purple range. *C. autumnale* 'Roseum-plenum' is a warm shade of pink: several flowers are produced by a single corm. Plant in groups in late summer.

Amaryllis *Amaryllis belladonna*. This species must have the protection of a south or west wall. It bears several splendid trumpet-shaped pink flowers at the top of a straight, bare 60 cm (2 feet) stem. Red and cream varieties are available. Plant in summer and do not disturb bulbs until new bulbs have formed. After flowering and when the foliage has yellowed, lift, divide and replant immediately.

Crinum *Crinum bulbispermum*. This species must have the shelter of a south-facing wall and needs rich, well-drained soil. In these conditions it will produce its spectacularly beautiful white lily-like flowers, sometimes tinged crimson. The spreading strap-shaped leaves are evergreen.

Crocosmia *Crocosmia* x *crocosmiiflora*. Summer-flowering bulbs that persist into autumn, Crocosmias (or Montbretias as they used to be known) are excellent cut flowers whose colour range – yellows, oranges and reds – typifies autumn tints. A member of the Iris family, the leaves are tall and flexible, the stems about 1 m (3 feet) long and the numerous flowers borne in drooping trumpets at the end. In an open border, they will appreciate the protection of herbaceous perennials. Plant in early spring in sandy soil with good drainage and water well in the flowering season.

Cyclamen *Cyclamen neapolitanum*. This low-growing hardy species is ideal for growing in woodland conditions – this means it will pair very well with Rhododendron bushes. In small gardens, too, it will thrive if given shelter from the sun's glare, protection from the winds and an annual dressing of well-rotted leaf mould after the foliage has died down. The 15 cm (6 inch) high pink flowers are long survived by silvery green leaves which last from the

autumn flowering period well into the following spring. 'Album' is a white variety. Plant in large groups in early autumn.

Lily *Lilium speciosum.* This favourite with flower arrangers is best suited for indoor pot culture, but may succeed in the garden if the soil is free of lime and a south-facing, slightly sloping site can be devoted to a group of them. At 1.2–2 m (4–6 feet) some support is required and protection from wind should be given. The species bears nodding white flowers; in *L. s. rubrum* they are rosy pink flushed deep rose and streaked purple. Plant in autumn.

Nerine *Nerine bowdenii.* Exotic globes of pink flowers are carried at the head of 60 cm (2 feet) straight stems. Plant in late summer or spring, preferably in a well-drained spot in the shelter of a south-facing wall. Lift, divide and replant the bulbs when overcrowding makes them less productive.

Sternbergia The two autumn-flowering species are *S. clusiana,* the flowers of which are 10 cm (4 inches) long, and *S. lutea,* 5 cm (2 inches) long. Both closely resemble Crocuses, are deep rich yellow in colour, and reach 15 cm (6 inches) high. Plant in early autumn in a sunny position in well-drained soil. The plants should not be disturbed unless overcrowding demands it. When this happens, lift, divide and replant at once to prevent the bulbs drying out. Carry out this operation just before flowering time.

Love-lies-bleeding *Amaranthus caudatus* is grown for its spectacular drooping scarlet flowers, like tassels, up to 45 cm (18 inches) long. The whole plant may reach 1.2 m (4 feet) in height. In *A. c.* 'Viridis' the flowers are pale green. Sow in April where they are to flower, in deep rich soil in full sun.

Salvia *Salvia horminum.* Varieties of this species have insignificant flowers, but the bracts embracing them are of great colour interest. In 'Blue Beard' they are deep purple; 'Oxford Blue', deep blue; 'Pink Sundae', pinky-red. The 'Monarch Bouquet' mixture includes a white strain as well. Sow seed outdoors from March to May, in a sunny position, where the plants are to flower.

Zinnia *Zinnia elegans.* Several hybrids and varieties have been developed from the purple-flowered species. The flowers are daisy-like and many petalled; plants reach about 60 cm (2 feet) though dwarf forms are available. The 'dahlia-flowered' strain with its wide choice of colours is a favourite: yellow, orange, red, purple, white, and green ('Envy'). 'Pumila' Zinnias are particularly good for cutting; the double flowers are smaller than the dahlia-flowered types and the plants only 38 cm (15 inches) high. Sow seed under glass in March and harden off gradually before planting out in May. Zinnias need sun and protection from winds and will not thrive in areas of heavy rainfall.

ANNUALS

Cup and Saucer Vine *Cobaea scandens.* This climber is generally grown as an annual. It bears large bell-like flowers of purple or white, with prominent stamens. Each flower is surrounded by a green calyx. The tendrils which enable the plant to climb enhance its appeal in trailing arrangements. Plant in summer in a sunny, sheltered position where the support of a trellis, netting, mesh or canes can be provided. More flowers will appear if the soil is not too rich. When the flower has dropped, the calyx also looks very attractive in an arrangement.

PERENNIALS

Acanthus *Acanthus mollis.* Commonly known as Bear's Breeches, these border plants reach 1 m (3 feet) with their spires of white or purple flowers and bracts. The large leaves, forming a bushy rosette at the base, are glossy and deeply cut. Plant between autumn and spring in well-drained soil on a sunny site. Cut the stems down after flowering. Do not disturb the plants unless they become overcrowded. They are excellent for dry arrangements.

Achillea (Yarrow). One of the best forms of Yarrow to grow for dried decorations is *A. filipendulina* and its varieties, all about 1 m (3 feet), spreading about 60 cm (24 inches) and bearing flat heads of yellow flowers. *A. taygetea* is good for cutting, though shorter, at about 45 cm (18 inches). The leaves are silver and fern-like. Plant between autumn and spring in well-drained soil on a sunny site. Cut the stems down after flowering.

Aster *Aster novi-belgii*. Popularly known as Michaelmas Daisies, the species of perennial Asters have a colourful homely charm reminiscent of cottage gardens. At an average height of 1.2 m (4 feet), the support of bushy twigs is called for, and as the plants deteriorate quickly they should be divided and healthy stock replanted every 3 years. Keep an eye on young plants for signs of verticillium wilt or black root rot, which will show as browning of the leaves. Cut off and burn affected parts. *A. novae-angliae* is the most robust species and should be given a sunny, open site in fertile well-drained soil. Pinks and lilacs are found in the varieties 'Barr's Pink', 'Harrington's Pink', 'September Ruby' and 'Treasure'. Plant between October and March.

Chrysanthemum Unless you really do have plenty of time to spare, and a greenhouse, confine your choice to the outdoor, so-called 'early-flowering' varieties. It makes sense to cultivate varieties not so commonly offered by florists. Since the choice is enormous, it is wise to visit a specialist nursery. A good pink selection is the reflexed, large-flowered 'Tracy Waller'. These types reach about 1.2 m (4 feet) in height and need tying in to stakes. They are difficult to assimilate into planting schemes not only because of their habit but their need for attention means they must be easy to get at. Plant in late spring in moist soil; keep tying in the plants to their stakes as they grow. Water well and regularly, and feed with liquid manure once a week till the buds are flushed with colour. Cut the stems right down after flowering.

Cimicifuga For autumn flowering it is worth growing *C. foetida* 'Elstead Variety', 1.2 m (4 feet). It bears nodding plumes of tiny white flowers on slender stems above abundant fern-like leaves. They like moist soil and a slightly shaded position. Plant from autumn to spring and cut the stems down after flowering.

Gentian *Gentiana* spp. The intense blue of Gentians is incomparable. Many variations of flower form and habit are displayed amongst the species, but of most interest to the arranger are: *G. asclepiadea*, which grows best in damp shady places and bears fine arching stems, 38–60 cm (15–24 inches) long, well clothed with foliage and 2.5 cm (1 inch) flowers in late summer, and *G. sino-ornata* (height 15 cm/6 inches) which thrives in acid soil and bears a profusion of 5 cm (2 inch) flowers in autumn. Plant in spring in deep soil into which plenty of leaf-mould has been worked. Keep well-watered in summer.

Geranium The Crane's-bills, as these attractive plants are commonly called, should not be confused with the popular pot plants which are more correctly called Pelargoniums. *G. pratense* at about 60 cm (24 inches) will need support but is the best choice. Varieties include 'Album', white, and 'Flore-pleno', double blue flowers; 'Johnson's Blue' has large, light blue flowers and is very free-flowering. Plant between autumn and spring in well-drained soil; Geraniums like sun but will tolerate partial shade. Cut down the stems after flowering.

Helenium *Helenium autumnale*. The central boss of these daisy-like flowers stands out so that the blooms seem to be thrusting forward. Most of the varieties reach about 1.1 m (3 feet 6 inches) and cover the range of colours which epitomises autumn. Try 'Butterpat', golden yellow, or 'Moerheim Beauty', coppery-red. Plant in any soil on a sunny site from autumn to spring. Divide when overcrowded and cut down the stems after flowering.

Hollyhock *Althaea rosea*. Another certain candidate for the cottage garden, Hollyhocks may reach 3 m (9 feet) when grown as a biennial. The familiar wide trumpet-shaped flowers may be any shade of pink from deep crimson to pale rose, cream or pale yellow. A heavy, fertile soil is best, and a site that offers protection from strong winds. Sow seed in the flowering site in summer and thin out in autumn. Protect the young plants over winter with cloches.

Bergenia The very large, broad leathery leaves of the Bergenia, so useful in the flower arranger's repertory, make it an excellent ground cover plant in almost all conditions. All species are evergreen; particularly recommended is *B*. 'Abendglut' (syn. 'Evening Glow') the leaves of which turn red-bronze in autumn. All species flower in spring. Plant from autumn to spring.

Kniphofia The autumn-flowering species of these very popular plants are generally more modest than their summer relatives, the Red-hot-pokers. Averaging only 60 cm (24 inches) in height, the spikes of little bell-like flowers are smaller and more delicately coloured – altogether more appealing to flower arrangers and gardeners who aim to give their garden a 'natural' appearance. *K. galpinii* is apricot and *K. nelsonii major* clear red. They need good drainage and full sun but are otherwise undemanding. Plant in autumn. Remove all faded flower stems. In winter, bend the foliage over to protect the crowns.

Pampas Grass *Cortaderia selloana*. A clump of these ever-

The autumn brilliance of the Glory Vine and Virginia Creeper are difficult to surpass. In this garden they mingle with the rich autumn colours of Hydrangea.

green grasses is often used as a centrepiece for a lawn. The long pale feathery plumes are, at their maximum 3 m (10 feet), spectacular; more versatile in a flower arranger's hands (which should be gloved: the leaves are sharp) is the compact variety 'Pumila' at half that height. Plant in spring in well-drained soil in a sunny site.

Physalis *P. alkekengi franchetii* (60 cm/24 inches) and *P. a. alkekengi* (30–38 cm/12–15 inches) are grown for their fruits, which are carried in the orange or red papery calyces which give them the popular name Chinese Lantern. Exotic as they look, they are easy to grow, and in fact must be kept in check by cutting back the invasive roots. Plant in spring in a sunny position in well-drained soil.

Sedum With their succulent leaves and mounds of tiny, densely packed flowers, some Sedums are extremely useful border plants. Especially appealing to the flower arranger is *S. maximum* 'Atropurpureum' (height 60 cm/ 24 inches) with its purple stems and leaves, and pink flower-heads. *S. spectabile* 'Autumn Joy' also has a lot to offer: the colour interest is in the flowers – 7.5–12.5 cm (3–5 inches) wide – pink when first open, deepening to coppery-orange and finally russet. Set out young plants in autumn in a sunny, well-drained site.

TREES AND SHRUBS

Amelanchier *Amelanchier canadensis*. This deciduous shrub well justifies the amount of space it requires (3 × 3 m/10 × 10 feet) in maturity. In spring it is covered with white flowers; in summer edible black berries appear; and in autumn the foliage is spectacularly red and yellow. No pruning is necessary. Plant when weather permits from autumn to spring, in sun or partial shade. Keep well watered.

Berberis Most of the deciduous barberries tend to have glorious autumn foliage and clusters of bright berries. The best species are *B. aggregata* 'Barbarossa', 1.5 × 1.5 m (5 × 5 feet), *B. x rubrostilla*, 1.2 × 2 m (4 × 6 feet) and *B. thunbergii*, 1.2 × 2 m (4 × 6 feet), with egg-shaped berries. All are easy to grow on almost any soil if in a sunny site. Plant at any suitable time from autumn to spring.

Cornel *Cornus* spp. Members of this family are very varied. The three described here are all of bushy growth. *C. kousa*, 3 × 3 m (10 × 10 feet), has white flowers and red fruits, like dangling strawberries; the foliage of *C. alba* 'Westonbirt', 3 × 3 m (10 × 10 feet), is red or orange in autumn, falling to reveal naked stems of scarlet; *C. stolonifera* 'Flaviramea', 2 × 2 m (6 × 6 feet), has lime-green bark in winter. Plant in spring in moist soil. Each spring cut the stems down to ground level.

Cotinus *C. americanus* (syn. *C. obovatus*), 3 × 2.1 m (10 × 7 feet), is of upright habit, and its oval leaves take on many shades of red in autumn. *C. coggygria*, 2.4 × 2.4 m (8 × 8 feet), shares this feature but is also rewarding in summer, with long plumes of purplish flowers. Both are easy to grow in a sunny position. Plant from October to March. Over-rich soils will inhibit colourful foliage.

Elaeagnus The very substantial texture of Elaeagnus foliage is an invaluable element in arrangements, providing a strong visual support for almost all flower types. *E. pungens*, evergreen, 3 × 3 m (10 × 10 feet), bears glossy green leathery leaves; in the varieties 'Dicksonii' and 'Variegata' they are edged with yellow and cream respectively; those of 'Maculata' are yellow with a green margin. Plant in April in sun or partial shade. Any soil type is acceptable.

Hydrangea The popular *H. macrophylla*, 1.5 × 1.5 m (5 × 5 feet), is the one most commonly encountered and it is especially useful for dried arrangements. The large round flower-heads may be pink or blue depending on the degree of acidity of the soil: pink varieties need alkaline soils, blues need acidity or neutrality. Consider also the graceful *H. paniculata*, 3.6 × 3.6 m (12 × 12 feet), the white drooping flowers of which somewhat resemble lilac, though they are much longer. Plant in autumn or spring on soil into which plenty of well-rotted manure has been incorporated. Protection from frosts is essential.

Ivy *Hedera* spp. The epitome of trailing foliage, Ivies can be made to assume both classic and informal characteristics. It is endlessly flexible and very useful in set pieces containing stone or wood. The choice of varieties is bewildering; for autumn colour the slow-growing *H. helix* 'Tricolor' is recommended; its pale green and cream leaves turn deep rose. Ivies grow almost anywhere where they can get support – from walls, tree-trunks, statuary and so on. Plant from autumn to spring.

Liquidambar *L. styraciflua*. The leaves of these elegant deciduous trees, generally trained as standards, are almost star-shaped and in autumn are brilliant vermilion. Plant between late autumn and spring in a sheltered position in full sun. Well-drained moist soil is best.

Rubus To this useful family belong the raspberry and blackberry. Their ornamental relatives, similar in habit, often have lovely autumn stems. When the small purple flowers of *R. cockburnianus*, 2.1 × 1.5 m (7 × 5 feet) have died, the naked stems are silvery-blue. Plant from autumn to spring in well-drained soil in a sunny site.

Snowberry *Symphoricarpus albus*. A spreading, deciduous shrub, about 2 × 2 m (6 × 6 ft), grown chiefly for its pure white, round berries, which are borne from October to February. The species *S. orbiculatus* has pink berries.

The Winter Garden

BULBS

Many of the species described below continue to flower into early spring.

Chionodoxa These members of the lily family are blessed with the attractive common name 'Glory of the Snow'. The flowers, in shades of blue, certainly look glorious on bright crisp winter days. About 15 cm (6 inches) high, they are best placed in large groups at the border's edge or in grass. First to flower is *C. gigantea*, with exotic-looking 10 cm (4 inch) wide lavender blooms. *C. luciliae* bears much smaller, pale blue flowers, but pink varieties are available: 'Rosea' and 'Pink Giant'. Plant in autumn in full sun.

Crocus There are some exquisite species of Crocus in cultivation, which reveal their beauty if anything better in a flower arrangement, where they can be closely inspected, than in the garden, where only a drift of colour is seen. Recommended are *C. imperati*, 10 cm (4 inches) high, outer petals cream with purple stripes, inner petals violet; *C. chrysanthus* hybrids, 'Blue Bird', blue, cream and white and 'Goldilocks', deep yellow flushed purple, amongst them; and *C. biflorus weldenii* 'Alba' with white pointed petals and startling orange stamens. Plant in autumn in any well-drained soil. The more sheltered the site, the earlier they will flower.

Iris Amongst the best of the early-flowering Iris is *I. stylosa* (syn. *I. unguicularis*), 23 cm (9 inches) high and with evergreen foliage. Pick while in bud and the lavender flowers will soon open indoors. This species will grow on the poorest soils if in a sunny spot. *I. reticulata* is one of the best-known low-growing winter Irises, also suitable for raising indoors in pots. The deep blue flowers are streaked with orange. Plant in autumn.

Scilla These very easily raised blue flowers resemble small Bluebells. *S. bifolia*, 15–20 cm (6–8 inches) high, is a deep blue shade; *S. sibirica*, up to 15 cm (6 inches), very brilliant, and *S. tubergeniana*, 10 cm (4 inches), very pale. Plant in late summer in any moist soil in sun or partial shade.

Winter Aconite *Eranthis hyemalis*, is a tuberous-rooted perennial bearing waxy yellow, bowl-shaped flowers on 10 cm (4 inch) stems. Good for planting in the shade of shrubs or trees, they should be set out in late summer in small groups. They need moisture, particularly in spring.

PERENNIALS

Bergenia *Bergenia crassifolia* has typically large glossy green leaves and is one of the earliest of this species to flower, with straight 30 cm (12 inch) stems bearing palest pink bell-shaped flowers. See also autumn perennials.

Christmas Rose *Helleborus niger*. From a flat rosette of pointed leaves a 30–45 cm (12–18 inch) stem rises straight, bearing a single wide white saucer-shaped flower with showy yellow anthers. *H. viridis* has flowers of sharp green-yellow. Plant in autumn in a partially shaded site on moist but well-drained soil. Do not disturb established plants.

Euphorbia *Euphorbia wulfenii*. Properly classified as a sub-shrub, this bushy perennial forms a richly textured clump 1.2 × 1.2 m (4 × 4 feet) of pointed blue-green leaves with spires of rich yellow rounded 'flowers' (bracts). To keep the form bushy, cut down the stems after flowering. Plant from autumn to spring in any soil in a sunny spot that is not exposed to biting winds.

SHRUBS

Cotoneaster *C.* 'Cornubia', semi-evergreen, is a good choice for the garden as it bears abundant berries that last very well; it is vigorous and may reach 6 m (20 feet). Smaller but quicker growing is *C. frigidus*, semi-evergreen, whose form *C. f.* 'Xanthocarpus' bears pale yellow berries. Good for hedging is *C. lacteus*, evergreen, 3 × 3 m (10 × 10 feet). All Cotoneasters are easy to grow, though they like sun. Plant in suitable conditions from autumn to spring.

Daphne *Daphne mezereum*, 1.5 × 1 m (5 × 3 feet), bears its clusters of small pink flowers on leafless, rather straight stems. The variety 'Grandiflora' has larger flowers of deeper hue. This species is easy to grow and is lime-tolerant. Plant in autumn or spring in sun or partial shade.

Garrya *Garrya elliptica*. One of the most attractive garden shrubs and of great value to the flower arranger, Garryas (height up to 5.4 m (15 feet), spread up to 3.6 m (12 feet)) have glossy, shapely green leaves and numerous long silvery catkins dangling from the branches. Easy to grow in any well-drained soil, Garryas should be planted in spring, if possible where they will enjoy the protection of a south-facing wall.

Heather *Erica* spp. This large family of evergreen shrubs includes very low-growing species such as *E. carnea* (prostrate or up to 30 cm (12 inches)) and the tall – 1–1.2 m (3–4 feet) – *E. mediterranea* varieties with a spread of 1.2 m (4 feet). Your choice depends on the amount of space available. Yellow, pink or white varieties are available, some with leaves that are bronze rather than green, such as *E. carnea* 'Loughrigg', with rose-pink flowers. The flowering season of *E. mediterranea* lasts well into the following spring. Two winter-flowering Heathers worth growing are the hybrid 'Arthur Johnston', 45 cm (18 inches), with rich pink flowers, and *E. carnea* 'December Red', 30 cm (12 inches), purplish-red. Heaths and Heathers like peaty, acid soils best but these few aforementioned will give satisfactory results on chalky land. Give them a sunny, open site. Plant in autumn or spring. Keep the soil consistently moist.

Holly *Ilex* spp. In order for Holly bushes to produce berries, male and female plants must be grown side by side. The best way to do this is to use them as hedging plants. They may reach 7.6 m (25 feet) in height, with a spread of 3.6 m (12 feet). Choose varieties of *I. aquifolium*. 'Aureo-marginata', 5.5 × 3 m (18 × 10 feet), has male and female trees, the leaves edged gold. A good pair is 'Golden Queen' (male) and 'Handsworth New Silver' (female): both form bushes broadest at the base. The leaves of the former are edged gold, those of the latter edged silver. To maintain their variegated foliage these varieties need sun; otherwise they have no special requirements. Plant in autumn or spring.

Honeysuckle *Lonicera* spp. *L. fragrantissima*, 2 × 2 m (6 × 6 feet), is a favourite among winter-flowering shrubs for its sweet fragrance. The flowers are cream. Plant when weather conditions permit from autumn to spring in ordinary soil in sun or partial shade.

Mahonia (Oregon Grape) The evergreen foliage of Mahonias, rather like Holly but less spiny, is what flower arrangers prize them for, but their racemes of yellow flowers are no less decorative, whether pendent, as in the hybrid 'Charity', 2.4 × 2.4 m (8 × 8 feet) or full and fluffy, as in *M. aquifolium*, 1 × 1.5 m (3 × 5 feet). Plant in autumn or spring in sun or partial shade in fertile soil.

Pieris In the winter months it is the foliage of the evergreen species *P. formosa* and *P. japonica* which is useful. The leaves are pointed oblongs and bronze-red when young, gradually turning deep glossy green as they mature. When the drooping white flowers appear in spring, the three colours together are stunning. Plant in autumn or spring in a sheltered spot in partial shade. These species will not tolerate lime.

Prunus *P. subhirtella* 'Autumnalis'. This ornamental cherry blooms the winter through, bearing clusters of white flowers on leafless branches. See spring entry for planting requirements.

Viburnum One of the most reliable of these useful winter-flowering species in cultivation is *V. x bodnantense* and 'Dawn' is a beautiful variety at 3 × 3 m (10 × 10 feet). *V. tinus*, known as Laurustinus, 2.1 × 2.1 m (7 × 7 feet), is evergreen, and bears large round flower-heads. Both are white-flowered and particularly useful for flower arrangements. Plant where there is protection from sharp winds. *V. x bodnantense* may be planted at any time from autumn to spring; *V. tinus* in autumn or spring.

Winter Jasmine *Jasminum nudiflorum*. An old favourite, this charming climber bears its yellow flowers cheerfully almost anywhere, if given support and some protection from winds. It will reach about 3 m (10 feet). Plant from autumn to spring.

Winter Sweet *Chimonanthus praecox*. This bushy shrub 3 × 3 m (10 × 10 feet), bears its heavily scented yellow flowers on leafless branches. 'Grandiflorus' is a variety with red centres to the flowers. It is slow-growing and needs to be near a south- or west-facing wall. It can be trained against the wall, in which case hard pruning is necessary after flowering. Plant from autumn to spring.

Witch-Hazel *Hamamelis* spp. One of the best trees for autumn and winter colour, the distinctive spider-shaped flowers of Witch-Hazel further endear it to flower arrangers. Most species achieve about 2.4 m (8 feet) in height, branches spreading about 2 m (6 feet). *H. x intermedia* varieties and *H. mollis* are recommended. Plant from autumn to spring in neutral or acid soils.

Index

139

Acknowledgments

General Editor: Diana Walker
Gardening Editor: Suzy Powling

The Publishers wish to thank the following individuals and organizations for their kind permission to reproduce the photographs in this book:

Special photography by Steve Bicknell; Pat Brindley 124; Julia Clements 84, 85, 88–9, 92; Jon Harris 13, 16-17, 65; NAFAS 33 (Arrangement by Mrs J. Dugay, photography by Howard Nutt); Herbie Schmitz 76-7, 81 below, 93, 96; The Harry Smith Horticultural Photographic Collection 104-5, 112, 113, 117, 120, 125, 129, 133, 137; Endpapers based on a design for wallpaper by Osborne and Little.